Lunch a

(NEW WRITING SCOTLAND 20)

Edited by

MOIRA BURGESS
and
HAMISH WHYTE

with Kevin MacNeil (Gaelic Adviser)

Association for Scottish Literary Studies

Association for Scottish Literary Studies
c/o Department of Scottish History, 9 University Gardens
University of Glasgow, Glasgow G12 8QH
www.asls.org.uk

First published 2002

British Library Cataloguing in Publication Data

A CIP record for this book is available
from the British Library

ISBN 0–948877–51–0

The Association for Scottish Literary Studies
acknowledges the support of the Scottish Arts Council
towards the publication of this book

Typeset by Roger Booth Associates, Hassocks, West Sussex

Printed by Bell & Bain Ltd, Glasgow

CONTENTS

4

David Neilson	Strathclyde Banquets	106
Kathleen O'Rourke	Marmite	118
Walter Perrie	Gifts	125
Andrew Philip	Nectarines	126
Lydia Robb	Subtopia	127
Hugh Clark Small	Mirror Life, Mirror Death	128
Julie Smith	The Bee-Hive Brae	134
Kenneth Steven	Kittens	135
Tia Thomson	These Gentle Days	136
Valerie Thornton	In Cahoots with Allah	137
	If only Coll were two floors down	138
Gael Turnbull	The Lady Who Liked to Stroke Floors	140
Billy Watt	Foxgloves	143
	Vine Weevil	144
Helen Welsh	Purple Iris	145
Brian Whittingham	Nacho-Munchers and Dolly-Grips	146
Jim C. Wilson	Utter	147
Dawn Wood	Midwinter's Day, Florida	149
James W. Wood	For my Replacement	150
	Biographies	151

INTRODUCTION

'Lunch at Yes' suggests a number of possibilities. Is it simply a meal at a popular Glasgow restaurant, or an imperative to feast on the positive, or is there some other meaning to be found? Whatever, it's an upbeat title and we hope it is indicative of the good things on offer in this year's anthology of new writing.

The recently introduced process of blind judging of submissions to *New Writing Scotland* is proving interesting. A few well-known writers who submitted work were not selected, while several new and emergent writers were, many of the latter previously unknown to us. The editors consciously try not to put a name to the work in the preliminary reading, but occasionally the writing is so distinctive the author is not hard to spot. For example, anyone who has ever read an extract from David Neilson's (unfortunately still unpublished) epic tale *Robert the Vole* would have no difficulty identifying his work: there is nothing else quite like it.

Very often during the selection process themes emerge of their own accord: in this case, food, winter, birds, fish and, given the predilections of the editors, cats of course. But eating and drinking seem to predominate (another editorial partiality? surely not) and so the reader may go to 'Illusions for Coffee', then 'Lunch at Yes', visit 'The Happiest Place to be in Scotland on a Saturday Afternoon', experience 'Nacho-Munchers and Dolly-Grips' at the cinema and have 'Nectarines' for afters (and don't forget the 'Marmite') – or indeed have a whole range of tastes and interests catered for, including the amazing 'Free Presbyterian Dolphins'. Now there's a title that can be read in more than one way.

As the wonderful waitpersons in Yes say: Enjoy!

Moira Burgess
Hamish Whyte
2002

NEW WRITING SCOTLAND 21

Submissions are invited for the twenty-first annual volume of
New Writing Scotland, to be published in 2003, from writers
resident in Scotland or Scots by birth or upbringing. Poetry,
drama, short fiction or other creative prose may be submitted
but not full-length plays or novels, though self-contained
extracts are acceptable. The work must be neither previously
published nor accepted for publication and may be in any of
the languages of Scotland.

Submissions should be typed, double-spaced, on one side of the
paper only and the sheets secured at the top-left corner. Prose
pieces should carry an approximate word-count. **You should
provide a covering letter, clearly marked with your name and
address. Please do not put your name or other details on the
individual works.** If you would like to receive an acknowledge-
ment of receipt of your manuscript, please enclose a stamped
addressed postcard. If you would like your submissions
returned, you should enclose a stamped addressed envelope
with sufficient postage. Submissions should be sent by
31 January 2003, in an A4 envelope marked for my attention,
to the address below. We are sorry but we cannot accept
submissions by fax or e-mail.

Please be aware that we have limited space in each edition, and
therefore shorter pieces are more suitable – although longer
items of exceptional quality may still be included. A maximum
length of 3,500 words is suggested. Please send no more than
two short stories and no more than six poems.

Duncan Jones
Managing Editor, *New Writing Scotland*
ASLS
c/o Department of Scottish History
9 University Gardens
University of Glasgow
Glasgow G12 8QH
Tel: +44 (0)141 330 5309

Gregor Addison

PROMETHEUS

Thog e a' bhotail thar a chinn 's thug e sluig aisde. Bha e dorcha a muigh taobh thall na cuirtearan ach bha solas ann an uinneag do dhà fhathast. Chuir e glainne air an leabaidh far an robh e na shuidhe 's dhòirt e beagan den uisge-beatha a mach gus an robh deagh oirleach ann am bonn a' ghlainne. "Siud thu," thuir e ris-fhèin. "Cumaidh sin às am fuachd 's am masladh."

'S dh' òl e an uairsin, cnap mòr dheth, gus an robh e a' casadaich cho chruaidh 's gun sgàineadh a sgamhan. "Nì sin a' chùis air," thuirt e. Dh' òl e a rithist 's sil an t-uisge-beatha thairis air a smiogaid. Stad e an uairsin ag èisdeach airson mòmaid ris a' cheòl. *Mon Vieux Lucien.* Carson nach robh ceòl mar seo ann 'san latha an diugh? Bha Cèit den bheachd gun robh e às a chiall ag èisdeachd ri ceòl cho aosda 's a bha a' cheòl seo. Bha e fhèin ag èisdeachd ri ceòl ùr Aimearaganach 's a' dol gu *raves* a h-uile seachdainn cha mhor. Bha còig bliadhna aige oirre.

Aidh. Bha iad cho eadar-dhealaichte. Is dòcha gun robh sin an t-aobhar nach do mhair an gaol aca.

Cèit. Sùilean domhainn donn 's gun chrìoch. Bha e mar gun robh an t-saoghal air fad a' gabhail fois 'sna sùilean ud. Bha lasair ann nauir a rinn i gàire 's bha e cho lainnireach ris an solas 'sa ghlainne uisge-beatha a bha an dràsda na dhà-làimh aige. Dhòirt an t-uisge as a' ghuitear 's rinn e sgailc air an ùir. Dh' fhaodadh e an steall fhaicinn na cheann mar cholbh uisge fìor, a' soillseadh 'san dorchadas, air a chuingealachadh leis a' chuairt-tomhas fhèin gus a thachair e air an talamh bog a bha fhathast ro chruaidh dha.

Dh' fhaodadh e anail fhèin chluinntinn a' tighinn gu seasmhach mar phìobaire. Carson a tha cruth aige uisge ma tha? Nach neònach sin, gu bheil cruth aig uisge 's gun robh e fhèin a' sgaoileadh a mach a nochd air feadh na togalaich ud far an robh fuaim an trafaic mar thuinn a' brìseadh air a' chladaich? Bha e bliadhna no dhà a nis bhon bha e 'sna h-eileanan. Trì bliadhna bhon a bha e comhla ri Cèit 'sa *mhanse* aig a charaid Ailein a mach air an rubha.

"Feumaidh tu a cumail," thuirt Ailein. "Tha an tè ud sònraichte. 'S barrachd air sin, cha do thachair mi a riamh ri

boireanach cho bòidheach, ach mo bhean fhèin."
"Tha fios 'am," thuirt Iain. "Tha i breagha."
"Breagha?" Fhregair Ailein. "Is *understatement* a tha sin."
Tha lasair na broilleach 's na sùilean aice. Tha thu mar
Phrometheus, a bhalaich. Cùm greim teann oirre."
Rinn an dithis aca gàire 's dh' òl iad glainne uisge-beatha
mar dheoch-slàinte fiù 's a' tilg na glainneachan 'san teine.
Bha fuaim nan trafaic a' brìseadh fhathast 'sna cùl-faichean
eadar na togalaich 's chuir a' ghaoth crith air an uinneag 'sa
chèis a' tighinn a staigh aig aird an uinneag a' geumnaich 's a'
bùirean. Bha Ailein ceart mar a bha e an comhnaidh ach bha
Iain làn fhèin. Smaoinich e an deidh greis nach fhalbhadh i 's
bòidheachd ged a bha i cha do chuir e seachad ùine a'
smaoineachadh air sin no a' toirt an àire ris a bha Cèit ag
iarraidh.
Sgrìobh e dàin bho àm gu àm mu bhoireanach air an robh
e miosail nuair a bha e 'san oilthigh. Is ann as an Fhraing a bha
i 's bha i a' toirt dha rudeiginn nach robh 'sa bheatha aige
thuige sin. Bha rudeigin miannach ann a thaobh a' choimheach
ud. 'S ged nach do thuig e dè na bha ann chuir e seachad
oidhche an deidh oidhche a' sgrìobhadh ma deidhinn. 'S cho
luath 'sa bha rudeiginn ùr air a sgrìobhadh chuireadh e gu Ailein
e gun dàil 'son am beachd math aig a charaid fhaighinn air.
Thàinig e dhachaidh aon latha 's lorg e Cèit na suidhe air
cathair 'sa chidsin a' guil am measg na litrichean a fhuair e bho
Ailein 's iad sgaipte air a' bhòird. Sùilean domhainn donn 's
cìochan cruinn gheal bhlàith. Ach chlisg e nuair a mhothaich e
na bha i a' laughadh. Cha mhor gum b' urrainn dha bruidhinn
ach an deidh mòmaid shuidh e mu coinneamh.
"Cèit," thuirt e.
Thug i sùil-geur air. "Cò i?" Dh' fhaighnich i dheth.
"Cèit, chan eil dad ann. Chan ann ach tè air an robh mi
miosail 'san oilthigh. Chan eil fhios 'am caite bheil e. Dh' fhalbh
i – gu Paris no àiteiginn."
"Paris," thuirt i an deidh greis. "An robh i bòidheach?"
"Cèit. Cha robh dad ann. Bha mi miosail oirre aig an àm
ach dh' fhalbh sin 's thàinig thu-fhèin 's an deidh siud…"
"Thàinig mi! Bha e cho sìmplidh ri sin nach robh?" Bha
i a' fàs feargach a nis 's cha mhor nach robh i ag èigheachd.
Bha eagal air Iain a nis. Cha robh fios aige dè bha a dol a
ràdh no dè bha e dol a dheanamh.
"Tha mi sgìth dheth seo, Iain. Chan eil e ag obair. Tha sinn

air a bhith ri chèile fad dà bhliadhna 's tha thu fhathast a' smaoineachadh ma deidhinn. Dè mum dheidhinn ge-ta? Is ann comhla riumsa a tha thu ach tha thu fhathast a' sgrìobhadh ma deidhinn 's ag innse do Ailein a h-uile rud mur deidhinn 's a h-uile argumaid a tha againn. Chan urrainn dhomh seo a dheanamh. Iain. Chan urrainn dhomh." Thòisich i a' guil nas truime. Shuidh e far an robh e. Cha robh fhios aige dè a bu chòir dha a dheanamh. Is dòcha nan d' rinn e rudeiginn an uairsin, air a' bhad, nach biodh e an seo a nis na aonar mar Phrometheus ceangailte ri clach a dhealbh e fhèin. Ach bha na litrichean sgaipte air a' bhòird 's cha b' urrainn dha àicheadh na bha annta. Bha e cho soilleir ris an lasair na sùilean aice nach mùchadh fiù 's leis na deòirean a bha a' ruith sìos a gruaidhean.

Sheas e 's chaidh e dhan uinneag far an robh oidhche a' feitheamh airson tachradh bhuaithe. Bha lasair eadar na togalaich ach cha b' ann ach solas bho lampa air Rathad Paisley an Iar.

Bha cuimhne aige gun do chaidil e ann an seathair an oidhche ud. Ged is beag a' chadail a fhuair e. Ach nuair a dhùisg e 'sa mhadainn cha robh Cèit ann. Dh' fhalbh i mus do dhùisg e 's bha na litrichean nan laigheadh far a dh' fhàg i iad air a' bhòird, a h-uile facal den mhasladh aige nam broinn.

Mìosan an deidh sin bha e air cairt fhaighinn bhuaipe à Paris. Bha e neònach a bhith a' smaoineachadh gur ann am Paris a bha i 's e-fhèin an seo fhathast.

Bha a' ghaoth am measg na craobhan a nis. Dè bha ann am beatha, smaoinich e, ach tanachadh de mòmaidean, mar na craobhan ud an deach a ghearradh anns an Earraich, 's cion dòchais? Cha robh barrachd ann na sin. Ach uair, bha bòidhchead na làimh 's bha lasair na dà shùil aice 's bha ainm air a' bhòidhchead ud. Cèit. Chuir e crìoch air an uisge-beatha 'sa ghlainne. Bha e a' fàs sgìth a nis 's bha a' ghrian ag èirigh eadar na togalaich 's bha eòin a' cruinneachadh os cionn 's thuit na glaoidhean fàisneachd aca leis an t-uisge 's bhrìs iad air an ùir a bha dorcha 's trom 's mar chlaich nach athrachadh.

Tom Bryan

WINTER POSTCARDS, STRATHKANAIRD

i) This 'Field of Thorns' meant blackthorn, which once bearded the silver chin of the river. Bracken and reeds inherited that shore, rooting in the rich lime soil. In spring, the cuckoo remembers blackthorn and still seeks it. In winter, the geese recall its crease on the land. Finches still search for dark sloes, to ease the coming hunger. Trees shake with the nervous hunger of birds in the early darkening sky. Take these older memories, sow them deep enough and the blackthorn will return. The lazybeds wait patiently. A final view: one silver line on a russet field.

ii) Upper left: hazel, elder, holly, larch. Centre: hail, mist, rain, smoke, granite, gneiss, limestone. Upper right: rowan, hemlock, elm and ash. Foreground: sheep, dun cattle, finches, robins, thrush, blackbird. Background: sky (all shades of grey, spilled and running). A man in the centre of it all, black-clad, bent to the earth.

iii) Adders sleep in the ground. Rabbits inch forward, towing the reluctant fog behind them. Two vapour trails break the solid grey – jets bound for North America or Scandinavia. Rabbits freeze, starlings scour the reeds and bracken for food. The sun strains against the fog, then sinks into a stillborn day.

Ann Burnett

ILLUSIONS FOR COFFEE

Margaret hadn't realised that Illusions was so busy on a Saturday. There was only a small table for two free at the back and she squeezed her way through to it. She chose the seat facing the door so that she could watch the comings and goings. She would have preferred one of her usual seats at the window where she had spent many a pleasant lunch watching the passers-by but obviously today she would have to settle for this table.

She read the specials board. Soup of the Day was broccoli and crème fraiche and there was ratatouille on toast with a side salad. Margaret picked up the long, slim, laminated menu and glanced through it. Not that there would be anything different on it but just to go through the motions of selecting her lunch. Hot filled croissants, cold filled croissants, toasted sandwiches, baked potatoes. Fillings were Brie and avocado, sun-dried tomatoes and mozzarella, cheddar cheese and their own sweet pickle, asparagus and Parma ham. She knew them all but hadn't tried some of them, she didn't know if she would like them.

The waitress smiled at her in recognition.

'Could I have the soup please?'

If she felt like it, she could have a coffee and a tray bake after. The list of coffees was impressive. Espresso, cappuccino, mocha, mocha chino, macchiato, caffe latte, Irish, Gaelic, honey flavoured, Colombian, Java. She wondered if she would have a fancy one or just stick to a cappuccino. Mind you, it hadn't been that long since she had thought a cappuccino was daring. A year perhaps. Maybe two.

She glanced at the plain pine table, small and round with the white salt and pepper holders, brown and white sugars in matching white bowls and the simple white vase with a spray of fresh flowers. A carnation today, a pale pink with a touch of orange on the petals and a sprig of greenery. Everything was spotless and spoke of middleclass ladies with time to spare. Today there were groups of them chattering and gossiping discreetly but there were also younger couples laden with shopping from the big stores. This wasn't a place for children, no hamburgers or fish fingers or coke, not even a high chair. Margaret felt that the atmosphere was improved by this absence. It was quiet and restful and restrained. There would never be a mother shrieking at her children, a couple arguing loudly, or even a man on his own. She glanced about. Yes, there was one man sitting alone at a table just to the right and behind her slightly. He was drinking one of the fancy coffees and delicately negotiating a filled croissant. She turned slightly in her seat as if to read the specials board. He was rather oddly dressed in a highly patterned shirt with a cravat and a deep red waistcoat. Artistic, she thought. From the theatre. She had seen a huge van unloading props at the stage door as she had passed. She looked more closely at him. Was he famous? She didn't recognise him but he could be the director or something.

Illusions was filling up and well-dressed women were milling around staring at tables, pressurising the occupants to finish. Margaret sipped her soup and didn't meet their hungry eyes. The broccoli and crème fraiche was quite interesting, she thought. Delicate flavoured.

She might go on to the library later. But it could be busy. She wasn't sure if many children were taken to the library on Saturdays. It could be noisy. But there again, there were so many other attractions for kiddies these days – computer thingies and play areas – that maybe libraries were old hat. However, she thought, if a lot of people went to the libraries on Saturdays then they would be returning books and there might be quite a good selection to choose from. She'd read all Catherine Cookson's but there was that new writer she had heard about on Radio 4. There might be some of her books in.

A movement across from her made her look up. A lady nodded at her and said,

'Do you mind if I sit here?'

'No.' Margaret was taken aback, she had been lost in her thoughts and wasn't ready for the lady's arrival. The woman arranged her shopping and sat back to look at the board. Margaret drew her soup closer to her as the table was small and space limited. A few minutes passed and Margaret continued sipping her soup and glancing at the woman. She was trying to catch a waitress's attention. There were quite a few Margaret didn't recognise – must be Saturday girls, she thought. Eventually the waitress who had taken Margaret's order moved over.

'A coffee,' said the lady. 'A mug please, black. And later, I'll have a hot croissant with the salmon.'

Odd, thought Margaret. Why should she want a coffee first? Perhaps she's thirsty. She should have asked for a glass of water, that wouldn't have cost her anything and she could have had the coffee with her croissant. She looked at the woman and smiled when she caught her eye.

'Busy today, isn't it?'

'I wouldn't know,' said the lady. 'I've never been in before.'

'They're very good, nice and clean and the food's always fresh.'

The woman nodded and picked up the menu again.

Margaret studied her unobtrusively. She was a bit younger than Margaret and her hair was a coppery-gold with darker roots showing through where it parted. She should do something about that, she thought. It looks awful. Common. And her face isn't common. Nor her manner or her voice. She wasn't wearing any makeup either, she noticed. Margaret never went out without her makeup. She felt that a woman wasn't properly dressed without it. Naked. Margaret's face was dry and powdery but this woman's was almost greasy. Her nose certainly shone and her eyes had bags under them. Quite dark, giving her a sad look. She could have covered them up with some foundation.

The woman caught Margaret's eyes on her. Margaret quickly smiled.

'It's quite mild today, isn't it? Makes a change after what we've been having.'

'Yes.' The woman dropped her eyes as the waitress put her coffee in front of her. Margaret finished the last of her soup and wiped her mouth with the white paper napkin. She watched as the woman first added a drop of milk and then a spoonful of sugar to her cup. She stirred it and then scooped another teaspoonful into it.

She's not on a diet at any rate, Margaret thought. Though she could do with losing a pound or two. Now that she noticed it, she was a bit puffy around the face like she'd been on steroids or some other drug. Maybe she'd been ill. She didn't look all that healthy. She was a bit pale and she definitely looked tired. That would be what the coffee was for – to perk her up before her croissant.

Margaret glanced at her empty soup bowl. Yes, she would have a coffee and a tray bake. The waitress was clearing the table where the lone man in the bright shirt was sitting. He was getting up to go while a couple hovered waiting to take over his place. He smiled at them and muttered a few words as he passed. He was really quite small and thin, Margaret noticed. But definitely artistic looking in a slightly bohemian way.

The waitress had disappeared. Margaret kept her eyes on the door to the kitchen until she reappeared.

'Excuse me.'

Margaret had to wait until the couple's order was taken. They were taking their time about it and asking the waitress questions which she couldn't make out.

'Excuse me.'

Margaret touched the waitress's arm as she made to move away.

'Could I have a coffee and a tray bake?'

'What kind would you like?'

Margaret picked up the menu.

'I'll try a mocha and a piece of millionaire's shortbread, please.'

'They make very good millionaire's shortbread,' she said to the woman at her table. 'I can recommend it.'

'I can't eat things like that.'

'What a pity. Are you on a diet?'

The woman looked frosty. 'No.'

She's definitely ill, Margaret thought. Diabetes perhaps? Or maybe a hiatus hernia. But would she take steroids for that? She could look it up later at the library.

The woman stirred her coffee again and took a sip. She reached into her bag and drew out a crumpled letter to read.

Margaret saw the official-looking logo at the top though she couldn't read it through the back of the paper. She's obviously read it several times, she said to herself. It must be important. Or worrying. Perhaps it's from a hospital. She peered at the reversed logo. It looked like the one the big hospital in Glasgow had. Neurosurgery they went in for, wasn't it? Poor woman.

Margaret bit into the shortbread. It was sweet and gooey. What a shame the woman couldn't eat it. As if it wasn't bad enough to be ill, you weren't allowed to eat your favourite foods. Margaret had never really been ill in the whole of her life. Not that she wanted to. She'd done enough nursing of relatives to realise that. But this woman was quite young really. And to be so seriously ill. She wondered if she had a family. Kids maybe. Or perhaps she was one of those single parents. She wouldn't be able to work if she was ill. Maybe this was a treat for her. A snack in a nice teashop where she could escape her responsibilities for a while. Margaret looked at her. She was still slowly sipping her coffee and clutching the letter. The typing made it look official and there was a scrawled signature at the bottom. Definitely a doctor's. It was unreadable.

The mocha coffee was well, unusual. She wasn't sure if she liked it. Maybe it just took a bit of getting used to. It wasn't that she wouldn't try it again but... She remembered the first time she'd had a cappuccino. She had had a white moustache. But she was quite used to it now, in fact it was one of her favourites. The woman had had only a plain black one. She felt rather pleased that she was drinking mocha. It made her seem a bit well, cosmopolitan. But perhaps the woman wasn't allowed anything fancier than a plain black coffee. She probably had to be very careful. It must be worrying for her not being able to work and trying to bring up a family on her own.

Margaret drained the last of her coffee. She looked across at the woman, still sipping, still holding the letter and made up her mind. She gathered her things together and stood up. The woman didn't even appear to notice.

'Bye,' said Margaret.

'Goodbye.' It was as if she had to drag her head up to look at Margaret and then her eyes dropped back to her coffee.

Margaret went to the pay desk.

'What table?'

'Number 5. I had a soup and a coffee and a tray bake. Millionaire's shortbread. It was delicious. And I'll pay for the other lady's as well. A black coffee and a hot salmon croissant.'

'£9.75.'

She handed over a ten pound note.

'Keep the change.'

The girl smiled briefly.

Margaret made her way to the door, her step light, her heart uplifted. She imagined the surprise and delight on the woman's face when she realised that her bill had been paid. Jauntily, she stepped out into the street and humming a little, made her way to the library.

Across the street, the small man in the bright shirt and red waistcoat towered above the crowd handing out balloons to the children and smiling down at them from his stilts.

Jim Carruth

THE BALEMARTIN BARD

He could be gone for days

moving between the ceilidh houses
of neighbouring townships.

Even in his absence
they came to the croft,

the daughters and sons of cottars,
appearing in ones and twos

from the long grass of the machair,
ragged and hungry for new words.

Leaving the chores
his sister welcomed them all.

Her rough hands would point
below the sagging lintel

to the driftwood door
where he had carelessly scribbled

his most recent bardachd.
She would read it to them

as slowly as the tides turn
letting the music of each line

fill their ears.
In the singing voices

that departed across the fields
she would listen

for the echo of her brother.

Colin Clark

THE HAPPIEST PLACE TO BE IN SCOTLAND ON A SATURDAY AFTERNOON

You've got to be ...
Ye've goattae be ...
Ya *gatta* be ...

In The Mood
for Harry Roth and his Big Band Sound.

You nearly riddy yit?

That's Mary, my wife. She's always ready first. Every Saturday for, what is it now? – fifteen years? Since we retired anyway. Every week she's sitting out on the good sofa, worrying the antimacassars, telling me to get a move on. She never changes.
'Ah'm nearly therr! Jist fixin ma tie!'
Here she comes.

Ye look dandy, noo come on – the taxi'll be here in two minutes. An lookit the state ae yir tie! Ah wish ye'd lit me dae it.

Always the same. I don't think I ever had a chance to put that tie on straight on my own since we got married.
In The Mood. We got a CD player HiFi from our Gerry and Jean for Christmas a number of years ago – I don't know, what, ten, twelve? And what a sound! You want to hear this thing. A Grundig. Sounds just like the band's playing in your living room. She doesn't usually allow my music to get played at anything above a whisper, but when it comes to Glenn Miller and American Patrol, or String of Pearls then it gets cranked all the way up. And on Saturdays, of course, In The Mood.
Not my favourite tune, but the wife insists on playing it when we're getting ready to go to Harry's. I find it a bit too syrupy for my taste – I was always a fan of the be-bop. Dizzy Gillespie was my man. A Night in Tunisia – *ba dabada beeee dooya doobap!* And Parker – though for me, Diz always had that bit more grace. Parker was too showy for me. Still gets my

blood racing when I hear music from those days. The wife
prefers all the slushy stuff, Tommy Dorsey, Glenn Miller. The
Big Bands. It's the stuff that Harry plays, though, so let's just
say we agree to differ – just as long as I agree to differ with her,
that is.

Am I 'In The Mood'? This Saturday at Harry's will be like
no other Saturday at Harry's. I don't know if I can…

*Wherr ur ye? You no riddy yit? See if that taxi comes an
you're no riddy…!*

'Be oot in a tick, Mary love. Jist fixin ma herr.' There, a
wee splash of aftershave as well.

Fix aw ye like, ye'll be no match for that Tommy.

Tommy's Harry's singer. Gets up and does a few numbers
with the band. He's that good. A real star. He's Tommy Sinatra
for one set, Tommy Durante for another. A pompous arse, of
course – all the girls fancy him and all the boys are jealous but
he's still some singer. He's got Sinatra's Jersey vowels. The way
he does the 'ooo' in I've Got You Under My Skin. He's good.
Wish I had his talent.

Mary's always had the glad eye for Tommy. She eventually
got chatting to him a couple of years back. We'd been going a
while by then, but Harry's is like that – you see the same people
week in, week out, but you always end up talking to the same
wee circle. I'm not much of a mingler, really, but Mary was
always that bit more sociable than me. So she planked herself
next to Tommy one time and that was it. After that, it was up
early on a Saturday, hours before we're due to leave the house,
locked up in the bathroom plastering on the make up, dousing
herself in hairspray and perfume, getting dolled up. It was all
for Tommy; she gave up getting dolled up for me – seems like
ages ago now. She would never say, never admit to me, but I
knew. We both knew, but I didn't mind: I liked to see her feel
good about herself. Some things shouldn't be said, though, or
it breaks the magic.

Am I in the mood? I'll have to face them all sometime. This
is the third Saturday I've had this debate with myself in the
bathroom mirror, Glenn Miller blaring away in the living
room. It's the music poses the question. I've often wondered: In

The Mood for *what*? When I die and go to heaven I'm going to find Glenn Miller and ask him what he was in the mood for. (If he isn't still lost in the Bermuda triangle somewhere, that is.) What was it moved him? A tender moment? A heart-stopping glimpse? Anticipation of an affair? Nothing so poetic, I'll bet. The answer is probably as unimaginative as the tune. A girl. A dance.

No dancing at Harry's though, there's no room. We all get squashed into this function area, everybody squeezes round the tables, wedged into corners, trapped into recesses. Everybody has their own place. Eric's group sit to the left of the band; Len and his lot over by the fire exit; Alice and Irene and their cronies out at the front with a spare seat for Harry when he sits down. I sit with the boys over by the window. There's hardly room enough to spin a sixpence, never mind shuffle about to a big band. Nobody gets a dance except Harry: he's the only guy I've ever seen conducting a band with his shoulders. Him and his Florida tan and his retirement home patter. It'll be hard to dwell on the memories when Harry's on the floor.

Whit's keepin you in therr? Ye're no huvvin second thoughts, ur ye noo? No again. Come oan, misery guts! Wir gaun an that'll be the end ae it.

She's still at it. Harping away.

I love her. How could I not? Almost fifty years, four years shy. I got to know her every movement. Learned the rhythm of her breathing, the shape of her thoughts. For fifty years breathed the perfume of her presence – awareness, you feel it most in absence.

Am I in the mood today? I can't stay away forever. Everyone'll be there. Alice and Irene and the girls. Eric and Auld Lenny. Tommy. It'll have been hard for them too; I'm not the only one that loved her. Been going to Harry's on a Saturday for so long, it's become like a family gathering.

Harry's music. Tommy's voice. They won't bring her back, but ... they'll know. They'll make it easier. For all of us.

There's my taxi. Am I in the mood?

Aye, I'm in the mood.

Ken Cockburn

LEAVING CALYPSO

I don't suppose I'd have come if I'd known it was going
                                          to be like this –
Waterspout.
        Bubbling Springs.
            Fast Channel.
                River Run.
                    Beach.
                        Flumes.
                            Spa Pool.
A stage set
that looks as if it's always been here
when once –
hard to picture.

I enter naked other than trunks
and the wristband containing the locker key.
Flat feet flip flop on the floor
flesh on view to all of interest
to none, for all their near-nakedness
bodies here rarely allure
the unflattering costumes
hair flattened by chlorinated water
that masks all other scents
attractive or repellent.
Where do you swim?
I wanted to plough up and down
expand the lungs
but the kids dart back and forward
and there's no space among
coloured polystyrene floats
sharks and crocodiles
bodies with outstretched arms and legs
the corpses of the drowned
risen to the surface.
The living who inhabit this makebelieve seaworld
make a controlled commotion under the stringent gaze
of an attendant in shorts and polo-top

manning the console
This is a staff announcement
This is a public announcement
The wave machine is now being switched on
Would all non-swimmers, weak swimmers and swimmers
    with armbands
please make their way to the shallow end
all he needs is a trident
to complete the masque.

I shall settle for the Bubbling Spring
shuffle bum to get comfy
to avoid bubbling balls
already boiled over once today
and still sensitive
needing longer to get over the exertion nowadays
stomach larger and softer than of old
hair spreading across chest and thighs
as on top I grey and bald
but not unenjoyable
not unenjoyable at all
a degree of restraint
Mistress Sonia tie and tease
providing cues to which I give the scripted responses
if you're obedient I might let you
those little prompts nipping in
ahead of reason
and the critical faculties tend towards meltdown
I've started so I'll finish
straps and buckles
her shinyblack and skintight dress
the point of her stiletto across
down down down not good
to be erect with kiddies present so
think about about about think about tonight
tonight is dinner with clients
so no pictures of Mistress Sonia

in her tight and shiny dress and high high heels no
not at all instead instead
instead the fat and sweaty fellow
Malone or Molloy or Mathieson
check beforehand on the laptop
puce and greasy. Indeed.
Detumescence achieved.
Mr M. is to be greeted with a smile and a handshake
at 7.30pm sharp in the hotel lounge
efficiently but not hurriedly do the business
and ensure an early night
in preparation for the journey home tomorrow.

Good job these jaunts are not more frequent.
The sense of unrootedness that occurs on my awaydays.
Not to mention a drain on the housekeeping.
Spleen of lustihead.
I need to swim
get the heart go pumpumpumping
but here there's no space
perhaps out from the Beach
where there is clear water
for Poseidon has clicked the waves into calmness
and alas I am weary weary o
if you're very good.
Rollover.
Now then.
Will all swimmers with yellow armbands please vacate the pool.

The kids clambering up the steps to the flumes.
Charlie was always first in line.
How far away I've wandered.
Rattling around the world
like one of his teeth when he was young
or one of mine loose against the tongue.
Fairies at the bottom of the garden
among the lupins the tortoise liked
and a coin under my pillow in the morning.

Gas at the dentist
the black mask secured over mouth and nose
and that moment like drowning
before the hallucinations kick in
spacecraft spinning against the black
like on the Hungarian stamps
Magyar Posta, Ferenc Puskas
I had his ghostwritten autobiography
the World Cup final against the Germans in '54
in *The Wedding of Maria Braun*
they're watching it on TV
it's 2-2 with a minute to go
Maria forgets she left the gas on
goes to the kitchen to light a cigarette
BOOM and cut to black but the commentary continues
the Germans snatch a last-minute winner
and Fassbinder overdoses at what?
thirty-six, boom.
The house-lights come up
and we file out past those about to go in
blinking in the sunlight
and there on the posters
is Schygulla, adjusting her suspender.

The wave machine is now being switched on.
Everyone makes their way towards the Beach.
Stimulus and response.
The sea around me fills up with bodies
but that seagull on the ledge has its eye fixed
on none other than yours truly.
A gentle swaying at first that becomes stronger
Please stay clear of the walls.

A woman sitting in the shallows with a toddler.
Like Stella and Charlie once.
Crying at all the swishing water, her smiling reassurances.
His bafflement at being unable to hold it.
If I left them for good I could go visiting whenever I liked.

Tomorrow I'll see Charlie if he's around and Stella
doubtless a choice selection of those parasites
she never has the heart or nerve to turn away
can I borrow a book? the library copy's missing
my computer's crashed, can I log on through yours?
Food in the freezer, wine in the cellar, open house.
The endless metamorphosis of her bloody thesis
into a book she refuses ever to finish
revisions I need to make
in the light of new information.
O Stella, Stella, tell me your secrets.

Whatever, whatever.
Here I fall and rise with the waves
drifting where the waters carry me
to some kind of haven perhaps
or wash me away.
All in the hands of the gods
of whichever gods
might still have the grace to believe in me.

Allan Crosbie

PLATO IN POTOSÍ

Banished to float through time, he lives in shadow,
in every type of cave you'd care to mention
or imagine: the empty boots of cars, the cellars
of murderers, sea-worn smugglers' nests – he knows
them all, but feels most at home right here.
This place of torture's so like his own invention
it scares him, but who wouldn't be drawn to a metaphor
made real – the strange beauty of the fires
burning in the mules' eyes, on the hair between their ears,
on the slaves' glistening backs as they mine the shadows?

•

He dreams of the two young brothers in Bermuda
who, playing on their lawn, kicked a ball
as far as the garden's end but saw it fall,
before it reached the fenced-off cliff-edge, through a
hole hidden by clumps of uncut grass.
He dreams of how they parted the grass like hair
and took turns to squeeze through the gap in the ground
to see the stalactites upside down sprouting
from the rock to the cave below where tourists flock now
to stroke the dripping spikes when the guide's not looking.

•

There are times he wants to recant everything,
to plead with those he would have banished; he prays
that one will come and find this abandoned mine,
pull aside the beams and the danger sign
from the hole and fall through time with every step
until she's here and says, *Come up – it's over …*
He sits in hope, perched like an angel at the top
of a seam, at the end of a whip, on the shoulders of a slave
who serves the cruel pale strangers in this cave
who live in a world where the only sun is silver.

Jenni Daiches

REMBRANDT'S MOTHER

Any woman's face etched with years
can be your mother's. Any faded eyes,
burdened and red-rimmed, so long as they hold
their steady gaze out of that particular dark,
flecked with gold, crowded with coupling,
childbirth, blood and the fear of death.

How you love to paint flesh, skin that's lived in.
Every face reflects your own, old
or young, but the more years the greater
the reserve of grace. Did your mother
ever take brush to canvas or bold charcoal
to paper? Let's say your greedy, generous eye

is hers, that alone you are empty, cold.
Let's say you paint women who never know
they can live for ever in pictures or write
their way to eternity or speak to the future
in the tongues of music. You are her gift
while she, in her wisdom, inhabits the dark.

FRANCONIA, NEW HAMPSHIRE

We come to the house at dusk.
The mist has risen from the river
and now our feet scuff through wet leaves
in a smirr of rain. The house dark,
the chairs on the stoop empty,
the white paint cracked.
On the mail box, faded, it says 'R Frost'.

The grass simmers as we walk, the light sucked
from the blazing trees. A sign warns of bears.
There are no fences, a path vanishes
into the mirk, where poems are posted.
The husky breath of birches
is as heavy as silence.
It's not yet cold enough for snow.

Robert Davidson

CANADA GEESE

Out of the haar, in flight,
in formation, in position, each eye
on the white rump in front, each aware
of the white bar on a face away to the side.
Direct, speedy – the flock is two waving lines
passing between mountains, over salt water,
following the coast, a creamy shoreline
broadening on to marshes, tidal islands
until – ahead and below – something familiar,
another flock resting on a sand bar.
Down they go.

Down, level with the hills.
Down, level with the road.
Down, level with the shore.
Skimming over water the lead bird
working hardest, the wind from his wings lifting
the following bird, then the next until
they are all floating on air broken by the birds in front.

They lift to cross an island. Come down again
on the other side. Up ahead, white-barred heads
turn on long necks. *Take care! Take care!*
crying from the bar, and from the air the flight
calls back, *We're here! We're here!* The sky
between sand bar and flight filled with voice.
Take care! We're here! Take care! We're here!

Spreading their wings, turning them downwards,
they stretch out webbed feet. Everything now,
every part of them, is catching the air,
slowing them, dropping them.
Take care! Take care!
In they come as though they must scatter
the geese on the sand like marbles, but now
their dropped wings lift them and bring them
down again, slower now, one after the other,
feet planing across the water, all together

hhhiiiiiiiissssssssshhhhhhhhhhh!!!

to sit down on it, glide along the surface and paddle out
onto the sand, to become a feathery conference
of webs, wings, necks and beaks, all crying together.
We're here! We're here!

John Drosten

UNITY MITFORD

I have a photo of you
seated beside Herr Hitler
at an outdoor tea-party,
so captivated you seem
hanging on his every word
taken about 'thirty-eight'

all that was before the war
that put a gun to your head
in the Englischer Garten Munich,
its warm pellet your guest
beyond our western lochs and hills
those last shamed years

it is a sadness to me
your residence on Inch Kenneth
brought with it the taint
of that malign discipleship
to within a few sea miles
of the green island of Colmcille

but then you took pleasure
in discomforting others,
contrary and perverse to the end

as when my brother
coming home on shore leave
met you on the platform
at Buchanan Street Station,
and you in your coffin
going the other way

Jane Forrest

LUNCH AT YES

Want to come to lunch
with Poet Laureate
I was asked
the very Friday before Christmas
when all hell was breaking loose
in Glasgow city centre.
Went by car to work
bus to town
got there
with ten minutes to spare
turning right at the street
where we should meet
right place wrong turn.
Eventually made it to Yes
but they said 'No,
no booking here for Morgan,
perhaps down the stair?'
Perhaps up the stair?
Beginning to despair
of ever meeting this man at all.
Then reaching the summit once again
I notice two figures
standing outside, patiently,
not in the least bit bothered
at being kept waiting.
'How do you do?' he smiles
'I'm afraid it was too busy to book.'
So I give him a look
and run back down
to the rather confused waiter.
'Three for Logan?' he asks yet again.
But I honestly declare
'It's not Logan for three
just Eddie and me
and one other very important man.'

They look at each other and do what they can.
Must have been the look
or what my mother said about me
getting a piece at any door.
We order the same food
except for one mince pie
which ended up begging,
just begging
to be eaten or plain left alone.
Then having stayed too late
I dive off
leaving it to fate
thinking as I leave
that it had been
just the most
perfect
of lunches
ever.

Griselda Gordon

BÖSENDORFER

Wednesday morning.

From my bed I hear the *clack cluck* of the letterbox, and the flutter of expected envelopes. I groan and turn over, snuggle down again beneath the bedclothes. I don't want to be reminded. Cocooned in the dark and warmth I drift back to a time when I enjoyed birthdays. As a young child in Edinburgh, they meant a rare day with my father and a large party, a time when the house became truly alive: Dad puce-faced from blowing up dozens of balloons; Mrs McFadzean, the house-keeper busy in the kitchen, the dusty aroma of cocoa powder, the whir of the Kenwood, and the melting slices of pink and white coconut ice, lined like soldiers on greaseproof paper, so sweet they made you shiver. For the rest of the year myself, Dad and Mrs McFadzean rattled around four storeys of gloomy Georgian elegance like three lost buttons in a piggy bank. Mrs McFadzean was a kind and whirling dervish of efficiency, but a poor substitute for a mother I never knew.

My sixth birthday was particularly memorable. I wore blue patent leather Start-Rites, white lacy tights and a royal blue velvet dress with satin sash, which my father had chosen from Jenners of Princes Street that morning. He was different from any other father I knew. Tall and lean, he carried me to the shop by piggy-back, and I, towering above the crowds of Saturday shoppers, hugged him tight in the icy East wind, cheek against the back of his frozen head, which was as smooth and taut as a leather darning mushroom, for he had no hair at all, not even an eyelash. The Children's Wear depart-ment was on the second floor, a large carpeted room lined with gleaming glass-fronted cupboards full of dresses. It smelt of crisp new cotton and polished wood. A stern woman in black with half-moon spectacles took my father through the selec-tion. I followed a few steps behind, nose to the glass, and drew pictures in the grey haze my breath had made, while she pulled out for his approval endless smocked tartans, silk taffeta dresses with peeps of lace beneath the hem, corduroy pinafores, blouses with puffed sleeves, and Lewis tweed kilts as green as a Hebridean sea.

Back at home when my friends arrived, we played Pass the
Parcel, Oranges and Lemons, the Farmer's in his Den, then
gorged on the pyramids of coconut ice, mountains of Blue
Riband biscuits, cheese and pineapple hedgehogs and a chocolate fudge cake that teetered on a silver platter in the shape of
a magnificent fairy-tale castle. I spent the rest of the party
twirling around in my blue velvet frock, watching it billow out
and in like a jellyfish in a sea made for it alone.

Today, I am thirty-nine. Hey Ho me Daddy O. A legal
secretary in a firm of solicitors. Living on my own and still
single, apart from Brian, my man of sorts.

I turn over and a waft of cold air slips inside. Like commas
and apostrophes, other men punctuated my late teens and early
twenties, but all were short-lived and unmemorable. Those
who stayed around long enough to bring home were teased
mercilessly by my father.

'And who are you again?' he would ask, shaking his hand.
'Mark? Oh, no, sorry, he was the last one. Terribly sorry. Alan.
That's right, Alan. How do you do?' And he'd turn to me and
wink. 'The big bed's all made up, Janice. I won't wait up!' He
tried so hard to be liberal.

I fan out my arms and legs, enjoying the cool of the sheets
in the unoccupied half. I love my double bed. I bought it on a
spontaneous burst of optimism when I first met Brian. I stare
out at the wickerwork of bare branches swaying in the winter
sky behind the large bay window. The bedroom is the largest
room in the flat, light and airy with a polished wooden floor
and scattered rugs. A private, peaceful haven.

Brian was a blind date, rustled up by Maimie and our
friends from the soprano line of the Edinburgh Grand Opera
Society. I think they all thought I had no initiative. He was a
friend of the tenor lead, who looked and sang like a god. Brian
doesn't, but he makes my spine tingle when he plays
Tchaikovsky, Rachmaninov and Dvorak. He's a professional
pianist. And so disciplined. Practises for at least six hours a day.
He plays for me religiously once a week on Friday evening and
occasionally at other times, when not preparing for a concert.
The routine suits us both. He's said he'll pop round later for his
dinner and I've taken the day off work.

It's almost a year since we started what they call a relation-
ship. He lives in a small bed-sit above a Chinese supermarket
smelling of asafoetida and rotting pak choi leaves, where he can

practise away to his heart's content without disturbing any neighbours. A baby grand takes up most of his floor. On the night of our first date we had to clamber over the piano stool to get to the single bed in the corner. We were just two, shy, awkward bodies fumbling in the dark to a clumsy conclusion, but my stomach yo-yoed in a way it hadn't done for years. He said he liked the way I moved against him, that I had hips strong and wide as a Bösendorfer. It made me feel exotic, mysterious. Afterwards he took a shower and slept the rest of the night on the floor in a sleeping bag. Considerate of him, I thought as I lay in the damp tangle of sheets, listening to his snores from below. Recently he's started talking about investing in his future, and hinting that he might soon move in with me. Sensible of him.

Today, eleven months after our first date, I clamber out of bed, pull on my dressing gown and wander to the front door and the pile of envelopes. I pull out those I recognise: Dad's, Brian's and the scratchy scrawl of Maimie. I open Dad's first. He always chooses a reproduction from the National Gallery of Scotland. Since retiring he walks there most afternoons, and sits for hours in the Impressionists Room. He and Mum often visited it as students. This year's card is Renoir's *A Woman Nursing a Child*, which he's often told me was Mum's favourite. He thinks I once resembled the baby. I stare at the young woman in the plump, robust glow of motherhood, her arms curved peacefully round the suckling infant. Soft curves, intense colours, the enchantment of quiet domesticity. I open it and read.

'*Darling Janice, enjoy this birthday while you can. The next one is the big Four Oh! Pop in any time, sweetheart. You know where I am.*
P.S. Maimie visited the other day. Thinks you and Brian are about to get hitched. Wink wink. When are you going to introduce me to your mystery man?'

I place the card on the hall table, feeling guilty because I have not visited him for months. And when I do, it's on my own, although I can't imagine why he would dislike Brian.

I tear open Brian's envelope, wondering what card he has chosen from the rows displayed in the 'For my Girlfriend' section. It is a soft-focus photograph of a couple lounging in a sunny meadow, blowing dandelions at each other. She's wearing a floaty white dress. He's lying on his side, confidently poised to ravish, looking as if he smells of Persil. I expect Brian would like to be that man. We've never been near a meadow, though, because he suffers from hay fever. Inside the caption reads,

> *The warm and precious moments*
> *Of which memories are made...*

He signs his name in small precise writing with a kiss beside it. I know it's sugary, but I would like him to say things like that sometimes. Still, it's the thought that counts. I imagine him in the card shop, his clean manicured fingers selecting each one, gold-rimmed specs perched neatly on the end of his nose, thick eye-brows joined in a deep frown. He will shake his head as he imagines my response to each of them, deftly placing those rejected back into their correct slots.

I place his card next to Dad's and open Maimie's.

'For God's Sake, woman, I'm waiting. Ask him, if necessary! *Oh, and by the way, Happy Birthday.'* Typical Maimie. Always trying to arrange my happiness. I sigh and place the card next to the other two. The phone rings.

'Did you like the card?' He sounds eager, excited.

'It was a sweet thought, Brian. Really. Thank you.'

'Good, good ... it's just that, I know it's short notice, but I've a change of plan. Can you meet me this afternoon? I've a surprise for you.'

He gives me an address in Leith and instructions how to get there.

'Is it a shop?' I ask, puzzled.

'More of a store than a shop. You'll see. And wear something nice. I'll take you out to dinner after.'

I am not sure what makes my heart race more, the surprise or dinner. It's not that Brian's mean, but like me, he's careful. We've always gone Dutch, even on 'carry-oot' fish suppers from the L'Alba D'Oro.

'I can't wait.'

I hang up. My hand is shaking. I am intrigued, confused, hardly daring to hope. *Wear something nice.* He never minds how I look. But there's something about the card, his tone of voice, and the mysterious rendezvous. I race back to the bedroom. After rifling through the wardrobe and chest of drawers, I finally settle on a slimming black jersey dress and liven it up with a bright silk neck scarf. But I want to surprise him, too. I think for a moment, and it comes to me. There is an unopened package in my bottom drawer that Maimie gave me as a joke one year. 'For your honeymoon – when it happens,' she'd giggled. It's still in its cellophane wrapping. I search for it and pull it out; a red satin bra and knickers set, edged with pink down. Tarts' wear. I unwrap the garments, run them slowly through my fingers, under my chin. I take off my dressing gown and pull the slippery fabric over goose-pimpled flesh. I've widened a lot since the gift was given, and the elastic is tight, stretched to its limit. I shiver slightly as the down tickles my hips and the top of my breasts.

•

A row of redbrick warehouses lines the road on one side, an industrial estate and unkempt scrubland on the other. The taxi slows down as we approach the number Brian has given me. We stop at a green door with yellow sign: J. EPSTEIN and SONS. I wonder why he has chosen this place to meet. I get out and pay the driver and walk over to the large storm door. Inside I find myself in a small glass-fronted foyer. The sound of Rachmaninov emerges. A vast gloomily lit warehouse holds pianos of every size and description. They line the walls five deep on either side, like giant chessmen. Brian is playing a large piano right at the back. He does not see me. I enter quietly and walk across a polished wooden floor, past numerous uprights, baby, boudoir and concert grands and a few harpsichords. Famous names wink at me from all sides: Yamaha, Chappell, Broadwood, Bechstein, Neumeyer, Blüthner, Steinway and Sons, Graf, Streicher, Ibach. When I reach him, I gasp. It is a monstrous size with an immense rump and feet of clawed brass. Its mahogany casing is smooth and glassy. I slip into the 'C' of the wide curve, the place where singers stand, and lean against it, watching him play. The lid is open, propped up to the highest setting. I can feel the vibrations. I watch Brian as he plays: the gentle sway of his body, the even, fluid movement of his arms, the athletic yet nimble fingers. No awkwardness now. I look up at his face as the intensity of the music increases. His eyes, black and dilated, look into the middle distance. His mouth is half-open. I listen to the liquid arpeggios, the silver torrent of upper notes rising above the bass roar. Beads of sweat appear on his upper lip.

'Look how she yields, and responds.' He shouts above the rising crescendo. 'Just listen to the velvet tone. The depth of that bass. Bloody magnificent.' A fleck of saliva leaps from the corner of his mouth and lands on the casing, fizzing on the polished surface like the bubbles of a rising fish. I have never heard him swear before. The music eddies to a stop. He slumps over the keyboard, arms outstretched. There is a discordant crunching of notes. His chest is heaving, his breaths laboured. Then, still in his reverie, he sits up once more, closes the lid and runs his fingers along it, leaving a trail of perspiration. He bends down to finger the ornate carving of the legs, their scrolls and grooves and fancy cuts. I come round and stand behind him. The name LUDWIG BÖSENDORFER gleams in gold leaf Gothic script above the keyboard.

'Over-strung,' he whispers, 'Viennese action. In perfect condition.' He stands up and strokes the bass strings, caresses their coppery coils. A deep purring sound emerges.

'How much?'

'Fifteen.'

'Hundred?' He doesn't look at me. I mentally add another nought.

'Is she worth it?'

He lifts the lid again and glissandos with his right thumbnail down the keys.

'A fabulous investment. No question.'

'It's your money,' I say, shrugging and wondering why on earth he has never mentioned such a nest egg.

He looks down at his feet. His jaw is rigid.

'It won't fit,' I point out.

'Oh, but it will,' Brian answers quickly. 'You see, I've thought all about it. What if we make your bedroom the sitting room, and your sitting room the bedroom? Buy a smaller bed. You, me, the piano under one roof. Lot more convenient, n'est-ce pas?' He smiles in my direction, but his eyes avoid mine.

'Is that a proposal?' I try to keep the tremble out of my voice. He removes his specs and begins polishing them with a little yellow cleaning cloth from his jacket pocket.

'Isn't that what you've been waiting for?'

The elastic on my satin knickers has begun to pinch; its

feather trim sticks to my skin, itchy. I stare at the thing with clawed feet, which lingers in the gloom like some buxom Austrian hausfrau, legs apart, ready to be played. Her gold lettering glistens, beckoning. BÖSENDORFER. BÖSENDORFER. I turn and walk away. I keep walking until I reach the door. He does not follow, protest, or clutch at my shoulders, weeping. He will find another flat to house her. I walk through the foyer into the dark of early evening. The streetlamps have just been switched on. There is frost in the air, and I can see my breaths vaporising in white clouds. A lone seagull mews above. As a taxi passes, I seize the chance, wave to it and jump in.

I give the address and sit back in the leather seat, close my eyes and think of him. There is a slight hunch to his gait now, his skin is yellowing and wrinkled in places, and liver spots are appearing on the back of his hands, but his head still shines like a beacon.

When I get there I will walk up to the wrought iron railings and look through the window into the soft light of his study. I will watch as he sits at his desk beneath the conical light from his Anglepoise, head bowed, absorbed in his papers. I will wait until he looks up and sees my dark silhouette clutching the railings. Then I will smile at him and wave, before climbing the worn grey steps and entering.

Charlie Gracie

RANDOM ACTS OF KINDNESS

When I reach the bus stop at the top of the hill, I get off the bike,
glad to be out of the rain for a bit. Incessant. And the cars that
shoom! shoom! shoom! past, spraying me from the dirty road
and the children's faces peering through steamy portholes. My
denims are clinging to my legs and I can feel the damp beginning to seep right inside me. Sucking the heat from my bones.

I look back down towards the main road. On the left, the
street is lined by trees. Cherry blossom, hanging apologetically
in the rain. And just inside the park, a swathe of daffodils
weaving its way alongside the fence.

Three lassies run past me and jump the fence into the park.
I follow them with my eyes, until they stop under a cherry
blossom, trying to shelter under the spindly pink arms of the
tree. One of them turns round. Snaps 'what are you gawkin at
ya weirdo!' And her friends snarl – three snarling heads –
before they merge into one and sweep through the rain down
the grass, following each other laughing and stumbling into
the shelter of the huge trees at the bottom. Disappearing like
Cerberus into Hell.

On the right hand side of the street stand rows of big sandstone houses. They have grand windows. Their gardens tumble
or terrace to the roadside, all rockeries and shrubs and trailing
things, which spider onto the treadworn steps and paths. These
are the 'well appointed', 'sought after', 'rarely seen' places.

I jump the fence to pick some of the daffodils. There aren't
that many nice ones left, but I pick them anyway until I have a
good bunch. I lean across the fence and take two elastic bands
from the side pocket of the saddlebag and wrap one round the
stalks near the top and one near the bottom. I nip back over the
fence and walk into the bus stop.

Some sweety wrappers and crisp pokes that have been
swirled into the shelter by the wind are trying to hide in one
corner, nestling in with the dirt and twigs. The bench which runs
along the back of the shelter is painted blue, but scraped and
inked with mentions and a series of fuck thisses and fuck thats.

I shake the rain from the bunch of daffodils and place them
near the middle of the bench. They lie there, yellow and green
on the blue, waiting for whoever it will be that will take them

home, pleased to have made such a daffodil find on such a sodden day.

I get back on the bike and roll slowly along the flat. I look up as I pass their house. She is walking up with a bag of messages. In front of her, the wee boy is taking giant steps to the huge green door. Each is a precarious wobbly achievement. 'Good boy.' Each step she says 'good boy'.

I cycle past. I smile. It stops raining as I hit the downward slope, and in less than a minute I'm at the phone box outside the close. Before going up I get a twenty pence piece from my damp pocket and nip inside. I put the coin in the space between the telephone and the notice board. Just where it can be seen when you pick up the receiver. That'll make somebody's day. You never know what that wee coin could mean – a few extra moments to clear the air – or cheer someone up – or anything.

In the close it's dark and quiet. I bump the bike up the stairs and chain it to the railings when I get to the door. I have a job to get the key out of my pocket, the wet cloth grabbing my hand – not wanting to let go.

When I get into the flat, I kick the door over behind me and shout, 'I'm home, honey!' in a false American TV voice. I quite often do this, even though there is never anyone else in.

The smell of the empty house.

I go into the kitchen and take my fleece, trousers, pants and socks off, throwing them at the washing machine. My feet stick to the vinyl, each step making the sole pick up all the crumbs and stoory bits from the floor.

I go back through the darkness of the hall to the bedroom, where I dry the rain and sweat and put on some dry stuff.

I think about her for a moment. So gentle with the boy. I see her hair golden and her smile at him and the way she leans over to make sure he is okay.

I put on the radio. The seven o'clock news is just coming on, so I listen to the bulletin. Nothing. I switch it off.

I go out into the stairwell and take all the bits and bobs out of the saddlebag. Before going back inside, I put a battenburg cake just inside the storm doors of Mrs Carter's flat. I know she likes them.

When I return to the kitchen, I dump the rest of the contents onto the table and begin to sort them. Milk and cheese into the fridge. Carrots into the press. I leave the noodles out – I'll have them in a wee while. I look at the chops. Neat meat. Two grey pink slices in a blue tray wrapped in cling film. A logo proclaiming them cruelty free. I try to imagine what that might mean. Chops from a pig that's *not* been slaughtered? Maybe not. I put them in the fridge.

I like going to the supermarket. It's not really as impersonal as people say. It's just that there is no need to fawn. You could spend half an hour in the aisles, a nod here, a polite hallo there, people *do* talk to you if you're on your own and they're on their own and nobody feels the need to breathe down your neck or walk you home and nobody knows your mother or went to school with you because the best kind of friend is a friend for a moment when all the friendship can't be washed away and they don't get impatient and you don't have to go beyond the doorstep of their lives and they never want to come in and they don't care if they're not welcome and you don't either.

I sometimes treat people in the supermarket. It's great. Especially people who look sad. I might put a bar of chocolate in the trolley, or a cake. Last week I saw an old man with the most terrible flaky skin. I could see he was in agony, clawing at his old scalp and down the neck of his shirt, so I put a bottle of that dermatological shampoo on top of his frozen peas when he wasn't looking. I'm sure that most people don't bother to check what's there when they go to pay, so I reckon I'm doing them a favour. And it doesn't cost me anything, so I can keep doing it.

I walk into the living room. From the window I can see the city spread out. Alive but silent from here. The sun is beginning to appear from behind a huge grey balloon of cloud. It slants across the evening sending a thousand grey flashes from the rooftops. The breathless light of the dying sun.

As the globe falls towards the ragged line of roofs, trees and distant hill, it grows ever bigger and more orange.

A couple of starlings suddenly fly up and around the window in a flurry of squawking shrieks and sharp feathers. A bus in the road below squeals and hisses to a lazy halt, vomits a couple of passengers onto the pavement and chugs back off to the next stop.

I'm hungry. I go back into the kitchen and flick the switch on the kettle before spilling the noodles into a pan. I light the gas. The yellow and blue of the flame jets hang in unison. They work so well together, as if there could be no other way.

When the kettle announces it's ready, I pour the water on top of the noodles and stir the worms round and round the pan.

I put the chow mein powder on top and watch the concoction froth for a moment, then tip the lot into a bowl.

I go back through to the living room. Before eating, I turn the radio on. The room soothes to the strains of a tenor sax playing a dusty tune, held up by the softwood burr of a double bass and the gentle swish and tumble of brushed drums.

I stand at the window, eating the noodles with a fork from the bowl, looking out into the gathering darkness. The skyline and the clouds are fighting to see which will be first to extinguish the sun.

On the distant motorway cars begin to turn on headlights, so starting the nightly train of eager white lights one way and soft red the other.

I think about him. I hate him.

I see him hitting her and the boy screaming and him framed in the grand window pulling her by the soft gold hair with his ugly hands.

I go over last night in my head. Him vague eyed, hateful. Falling home one way then the other in the rain.

And me.

'Don't!'

His leering staggering face lolling side to side to side.

'Fuckin!'

He tried to make a lunge at me.

'Do it!'

I pushed him away, and he bounced off the wall right back at me.

'Again!'

I punched him. In the face. Blood.

'Right!'

Him trying to land a drunk fist on me.

I kicked him in the face. Once for all the kicks he gave her and once for the next time he does it and once because I've just fuckin had it with him the bastardin fuckin bastard and her face sore and the boy screaming – and him. I kicked him again.

The feeling in my foot as it hit his jaw.

Blood on my shoe washed off into the grass in the glistening hypnotic rain.

I looked at him lying there. He moaned and coughed, then tried to raise himself. I kicked him again in the body and he rolled down the bank, flattened out over bricks and rubble at the bottom.

My heart beat Didum! Didum! Didum! high and loud in my chest. The breath rasped hot in my dry throat. The rain soaked into me.

I left him there hidden and came home.

The eight o'clock news comes on the radio. Still nothing.

I think about what she might be doing just now. She is probably used to him not appearing, and glad when he doesn't.

Maybe in the morning when I pass on the bike, the police will be calling at her door. She will answer with the boy wrapped round her thigh, and they will tell her seriously and apologetically about him and she will cry or stagger or something but inside she will know that it was always going to happen because he was always shouting his mouth off and there *is* such a thing as a guardian angel and he won't be back any more to batter and bruise and humiliate and terrify.

Maybe, though, I will pass and he will be sitting bandaged at the window, and she will be bringing him tea and standing distant from him. And he will growl his way to fitness and prove his worth again and she will ache. And the boy will scream.

Rain hits the window. The snake of eager white one way and soft red the other twists on the distant motorway. The sky has merged with the distance and my room has a twin on the outside.

I open the window and slop the remainder of my noodles onto the sill. The birds will eat that in the morning. The noise of the night creeps into the room. The steady hum of rain and cars is interrupted intermittently by someone shouting or the bark of a dog or a horn blowing angry. Groups of two and three people pass in drenched huddles on the pavement, skipping like dancers as cars splash the puddles in the gutters.

I shut the window again and look at my vague other in the glass. I think about the wee boy. Screaming. And him, leaning down with his hands out, and picking the boy up and those hands that can cause such pain being the laughing hands of a father and it can just take an instant and you never know when and you never know why.

I turn and go back into the kitchen. I fill the noodle pot with water and put the bowl into it. I'll get that in the morning.

Yvonne Gray

GLENCOE SPRING 1692

I was there that night
stepped knee deep in the icy river
washing the clothes in the pure water.
I watched it flowing over the stones
and winding on out of the glen
to the land beyond, gleaming in snowlight
that fell from the shrouded mountains.

You saw me there that night
as you crouched by the shore of the icy river
scooping the dark flowing water.
You thought you knew who I was for you started
and turned away, your arm shielding
your pitcher of water as you ran, stumbling
through the snow, back to the village.

I was there that night
stooped knee deep in the icy river
washing soiled clothes in the pure water,
but I could not have stopped what was coming.
I watched you hurrying through the spindrift
seeing you fade as it soughed and shifted,
lifting before the gathering wind.

Long before dawn the spring storm came.
I saw bright suns as they burst on frozen roofs
and sudden red flowers that bloomed in the snow.
I saw the clothes rent with thorns
and wreathed with dark, heavy scented roses.
I stooped knee deep and washed them in the pure water
of the icy river that wound on out of the glen.

Iain Fraser Grigor

SNOW ON HIGH GROUND

FIRST DAY of the week, last week of the fishing year; and so
they cleared the harbour and put to sea, without hope, for the
last few weeks had been blank, as if the herring for ever had
gone from the ocean. On first watch, the Old Timer loafed in
the wheelhouse; abaft it, the boy-Cook in his galley (mince,
Gold Leaf and a new war comic) was making the tea; down aft,
the Big Fella and the Skipper were in their curtained bunks,
studying the newspapers of the previous week.

That night they got nothing, and they saw no marks till
dusk the following day, close-in to an island, with a slash of
wind screaming over its cliffs and shrouds of spindrift blasting
into the growing night. They had a tow, tore the net, and left it
in tatters aft. Later, in a sheltered bay and just as it began to
snow, they hauled the net forward and mended it. By the time
they had finished the snow had stopped, though it was colder
than ever. When they went to sea again, it was blowing harder
than ever too.

The Cook produced a meal, which he described as venison
chops, and which was even more of a disaster than usual. But
the Skipper, poker-faced, said, 'You're fair coming on at the
cooking, Cook': for he too had once been a boy-cook at the
fishing. And he knew that for pure nastiness the job would be
hard to surpass, and was rendered possible only by the fierce
intimidation offered by the crew to the slightest sign of inde-
pendence on the part of the boy.

In the wheelhouse, the Old Timer turned the boat through
the wind and she lurched violently. A basin of beans, a bag of
sugar and the tomato sauce hurled themselves off the cabin
table. Someone caught the sugar, but the beans exploded on the
seat locker, and the sauce lay smashed and bleeding at the foot
of the heavy steel heating stove. No one said anything: speech
was an effort, against the roar of the engine. The boy could clear
it all up later, as usual.

The Big Fella suddenly roared at him across the table:
'What's for pudding, Cook?'

The boy threw himself waist-deep in an appropriate locker,
reappeared, turned and shrieked, 'Peaches.'

'What kind?' screamed the Big Fella, incandescent with

mock fury.

The Cook jumped visibly, gaped for a moment, and then, with split-second inspiration and perfect seriousness, bawled back – 'Sliced?'

Later, at anchor somewhere, the men slept while the boy was left in the wheelhouse to get the forecast at the back of midnight.

'What was it?' asked the Skipper when he came up.

'Em – just snow on high ground,' said the Cook, with confident precision.

There was a terrible silence on the Skipper for a moment, a terrible stillness, in the winking gloom of his wheelhouse.

But all he said was, 'That'll be handy, Cook. You better give the boys a shout now.'

And so they went to work again. Each knew that the weather promised gales and worse on the way, but the night was still clear and the tops of the hills on the mainland coast were indeed white with new snow. In the far north the borealis were dancing weirdly, very high in the sky. The Old Timer was standing in the door of the casing watching them, with the Cook at his back, taking a break from brewing serious tea in the galley kettle.

'Do you know what that means, Cook?' he demanded, taking a cigarette uninvited from the boy's mouth, to smoke it himself. 'Ice. When you see them like that, it means bad ice up north.'

The boy, jaunty with pleasure at the recognition of his presence, lit another Gold Leaf and peered aft, over the boat's wake, into the north – towards which, in due course, he spat with stylish expertise.

'The hardest man I ever saw was up there,' the Old Timer said. 'In Spitzy. A German. Just after the war. We were in four days sheltering from weather when this rust-bucket side-winder came in. Rust and ice from stem to stern. God knows how she survived it. Her skipper came out on the bridge wing to have a look at the place. I was never nearer to him than fifty yards. But there was something queer about him. About the way he cocked his eye at the weather. He wasn't afraid of it, somehow. Anyway, he was at sea up there right through the war. All that time, up there on a U-boat.'

'What kind's a you-boat?' the Cook wondered.

The Old Timer flicked his cigarette over the transom and

into the boiling wake. 'He had a lot of friends in those waters, the poor bastard,' he said; and went down the trap at once, into his bunk, closed the curtains, and retrieved from its hiding-place a half-empty half-bottle of sweet, black rum.

There was no herring found that night either, and after lying in the lee of the land for the following day, they put to sea again late in the afternoon – a clear and crisp day, with shadows already on the hills in the east, and to the west the tops of the islands scattered like antique bonnets along the horizon.

The Big Fella, in good form, pointed to one of these far grey-blue tops, and told the Cook about a girl he once had known from its western side. The boy looked doubtful, as if fearful of complicity in something not entirely understood.

That night too there was nothing to be had, nor nothing throughout the following day and evening – by which time, down aft in the cabin, the gloom was tangible. Speculation began as to when they would turn for home and be done with it for the week, for the year – with just the prospect of the Christmas break ashore to blunt the pointed injustice of it all.

'What was her name anyway?' the Cook suddenly bawled at the Big Fella, over the roar of the engine.

The Big Fella leaned out from his bunk in his grimy vest and grinned, but shrugged that he just didn't remember; and at that the Skipper was hammering on the cabin skylight and shouting them on deck to shot, in a blatter of rain and the best part of a gale.

'But she had beautiful eyes,' the Big Fella suddenly volunteered to no one in particular; 'Aye, like an army with banners.'

They manned the winch and shot away, the wires lashing the length of her and singing with wild hope in the turning blocks, and towed away into the night, with the odd sea climbing the rail of her and rolling solid over the deck of her, and the Old Timer grumbling to himself, 'Just a waste of time, just a waste of bloody time.'

Close to some shore they began to haul, in a hurry, but the net unaccountably jammed somewhere; and before anyone could move, the entire sea right round the boat began to pulse with a sharp, translucent light. The Cook was visibly pale, even in the harsh brightness of the deck floods, as if he expected some creature from the world of his comics to climb calmly from the ocean and stand beside him on the deck. But the Big Fella was a founder-member of that society which fears little but human company and its wiles, so he leaned over the rail for a look with the tool-box torch, while the Old Timer held his legs for fear that a sea would carry him away.

'It's a mine,' the Big Fella announced at length, as if the whole thing had nothing whatever to with him, personally like.

'Don't be stupid,' the Skipper yelled hopefully from the starboard wheelhouse window, the peak of his tartan bonnet dancing for fear of what might happen to his boat at any moment.

With an air of wonderful nonchalance, the Big Fella heaved himself back over the rail, muttering darkly, and began to investigate the contents of the tool-box beside the cabin skylight. When he found what he sought, he snapped the wire-cutters threateningly at the Cook, who looked as if he might begin to cry at any moment.

'Boom Boom. Cook,' he roared at the boy, who promptly jumped with fright. The Old Timer snarled with contempt for the boy's fear – or maybe his own.

'Stand free of everything,' he growled, 'and don't hold on, that way you might get nothing smashed but your ankles, with any luck.'

The Cook opened his mouth; and before he could close it, or utter a sound, the Big Fella had snipped clinically through some wires attached to the mine, and which had been snagging it to the net. Then he stood back with a cool, experimental air, waiting for some sort of explosion; but there was none, though the neon rhythm of the sea went out at once. At that, with much grunting, the Big Fella dragged over the rail the offending mine, and laid it carefully on the deck. The Old Timer peered at it closely for a moment, and then snorted with professional disdain.

The Big Fella announced at the wheelhouse, 'It's just a Navy practice mine. That's what the sign says anyway. It has to be given back to them if anybody finds it.'

'The hell with the Navy,' the Skipper screeched from his window; and the mine, along with the remains of the underwater flare to which it was connected, went over the side without further ado.

'Cook!' the Big Fella howled in his most ferocious manner, and the boy jumped again with fright. 'Where's the biscuits?'

The Cook disappeared down into the cabin while the Big Fella and the Old Timer watched him through a gap in the cabin skylight. When the boy had buried himself deep in a locker in search of the biscuits specified by the Big Fella, the Old Timer took the heavy wire-cutters and hammered explosively with them on the roof of the cabin; at which the Cook came out of his locker and up the trap like some well-greased distress-rocket. Both men howled with laughter, and ordered the boy below again; and when he had slunk down into the cabin and into his biscuit locker, they played the same trick on him, until the Cook utterly refused to go below again, and spent the rest of the night in his galley, quaking and smoking and trying hard to smile.

Towards dawn there were more stars in the sky than even the Old Timer had seen before, and when the day began to come in, the snow-covered hills of the mainland were smeared with early fire, till the sun itself rose and it was time to head for home – for no herring were likely to be taken in the light of that fine, bright winter's day.

But they did not turn for home yet. With the engine eased right in, the warm soft beat of it dulled, they cruised south towards the land, and then turned north to thread their way along the edge of the skerries, hard in on the shore under the last towers and ruins of the old construction camp there.

'At least it's a Friday,' the Big Fella was saying to the boys down aft, when the Skipper called them on deck – and they shot, and towed for an hour, laughing at the futile nonsense of it all.

When they started to haul the sea-birds began to gather, and when the bag closed the surface the birds suddenly were diving on it from the wing-tip, in a wheeling and murderous frenzy.

'There's something there anyway,' the Big Fella at the winch observed with hungry weariness; and then a great tunnel of herring was laying alongside the boat, and all to come aboard: as long as nothing might go wrong. They began to take the stuff up over the rail, the best of stuff too, twenty, thirty, forty and more lifts, a greengold cascade of silverblue, against the angry squeal of the gilson and the scream of a thousand birds.

Then, as suddenly as they had come, there were no more – and the men on deck began to speak to each other for the first time since they had seen that great tunnel of fortune alongside, still in hushed voices at the luck of the morning.

They turned the boat for home, in for home and Christmas through the islands, her bows well-down with the weight in her, and the Cook grinning expansively as he made the breakfast. Down aft, the Skipper slept after a sleepless week, and in the wheelhouse the Big Fella and the Old Timer talked in muted tones, stunned at the waywardness of fortune, stunned at their largest catch of that year, or of any year.

By late afternoon, they were home. At the head of the pier, the garish tinselled livery of the fairy-lit windows in the village shops was strangely welcoming. They got a buyer for the catch almost at once, for a good price, the best price of the year. They began to discharge; and soon small puffs of steam were observed to rise intermittently from the hold. By the time they were finished landing, it was raining heavily, but the Cook was standing quite happily on the pier, arms crossed on his lumberman's shirt, two empty lemonade bottles at his feet, and a fresh packet of Gold Leaf wedged in the back-pocket of his jeans.

Suddenly, the buyer, oilskin armoured, came out of the rain and stood looking down at the nameboard of the boat bolted to the front of the wheelhouse.

He said, 'Why is she called the *Adeline B*, Cook?' after a pause in which he appeared to have been thinking deeply. 'That name didn't come off a Christmas card.'

The Cook grinned, as if party to some great intimacy; and then he volunteered in a spirit of magical inspiration, 'Maybe it did. Or maybe there was another one first?'

The buyer gave the boy a long, thoughtful look; and then changed tack.

'Where did you get them anyway?' he wondered.

'In the daylight,' the Cook said. 'Right in on the shore, at the old camp.'

'Oh, it's still there, is it?' the buyer wondered.

'It was this morning anyway,' the Cook said with some asperity.

'Aye, aye, Cook. Ah well. So that's the way of it. Christmas again, eh? One more, one less. It's a fair shot you have the day though. That's the biggest landing in here for years. The biggest price I've ever seen paid for them too. You'll make a pound this week.'

'We will right enough,' the Cook assented modestly. 'And we got a mine too.'

'Right enough,' the buyer said, mightily impressed. 'A mine too!'

'Ach, it was just a wee one,' the Cook replied with magnificent unconcern; and with every word edging closer to the coveted and elusive status that he so urgently sought.

Vivien Jones

BEING SUMI

In the woods my softness silences my passage. Hind paws touch where front paws were, three points of contact with a surface at all times. Up trees, which I love, the grip of claws and spasm of muscle propel me to safety. I tremble at the nearness of birds beneath me. I can cuff the birds from the air; what are they but weightless feather shells, two bursting heartbeats and a dulling eye? I can slice mice after I've bruised and broken them enough to prevent overmuch wriggling. Butterflies crackle briefly in my dainty jaws and tickle in the throat. This is my imperative.

In the house I sprawl in any soft or dark or quiet place. I sleep in several ways. There is my napping way, eyes never sealed, ears scanning and a readiness to flare my eyes at the smallest sound or movement. This is for when they are present or likely to be, for they are drawn to my softness and cannot pass me without stroking me. If I have found a soft, empty place I can make my circle, head to tail, head on paws, and shut my eyes and only gently listen. This is near to sleep. Sometimes, from here, there is a slow melting into an upside-down abandon in which my belly softness is uppermost, my paws extended, tail draped over the edge. If they approach with their small entreating sounds they can smooth my belly without awakening more than a deep vibration. In this state I fear I would not sense a dog's approach, though dogs are not subtle.

I wonder about dogs. With their obsequious wagging backsides and pointless noise and thrashing, how do they feed in the wood? I plan a badness to show my disdain for the racket of the dogs down the row. They, a pair of large dogs with foolish, eager eyes and flapping ears, want my fur in their teeth. I shall leap up to their window-sill, my tail perfectly vertical, my stiffened ears erect and walk slowly from one side to the other, not even looking towards their frantic leapings and scratchings on the window. They will salivate like mad creatures, crazed with hunting fever. I trust the glass. I may lick myself in congratulation.

There are few dogs in the night and those that do appear are the unpetted ones that know the night boundaries. A cat, however small, swallows the night through the eyes and perceives all spaces. I am, therefore, equal to owls and bats in navigation and therefore hunting, which is the purpose of night. Dogs abuse the night. They merely meander, sniffing and shitting, making noise as if without instinct. Dogs trade their instinct for a fireside and a meal bowl. I get both without loss of magnificence.

In the night there was a meeting with an owl once. I was in stillness, scanning a mouse's movement, waiting for a sight of its progress through the grass, when I was alerted by an air movement too late and too fast to be a small eating bird or a bat. As white as me, but from above, came a soundless fury, and several scimitar points as bright as my own raked my back. I listened to my skin for harm, felt the warning sting of several scratches but no heavy heart-beat to tell me to lie still and wait to die. I slid and hid my whiteness under a fallen trunk and watched. The owl came back, this time calling in its ugly voice, and settled in the tree above me. We battled out the silence; the owl less careful than me for I heard when he shifted his claws on the branch. I moved no part of me except for small flexings of my claws which just happened, but in silence. The owl did not sit long. This wood is full of things to hunt and eat, easier to kill than me (if not so glorious) and the owl must survive his encounters. Our claws are equal, our jaws are different, but equal. No gain for either in an equal fight. The owl and I choose to hunt creatures already vanquished by their panic.

I know I waited to die in another place. Before here there was a hard place with loud and sharp, unscented cars that were in constant flight. It was night but no proper night. Darkness tried to cover this place but light was there too. The cars had gone to rest and I hunted in the grass places where sometimes other cats growled, spat and sprayed. I crept low. From a gateway a hissing male raised his back fur at me in a territorial arch. Obligingly, I fled onto the hard place blind to the car so close to me, then on top of me in a fear-filled racket of disintegration. My leg lay down and then I waited to die. When the light came two crows and a seagull came too. The shining curious crows loped towards me, cocking their heads to see if I was hunted down, but keeping out of claws' reach. The seagull squawked its interest from a wall by the grass place. It already had blood under its salty jaw. The crows were sniffing my blood when, suddenly, all three birds flew off as voices sounded and feet came close as they approached to look at my death. Then came a time in a smelling place, near death but not death, and there were thin, hurt cat voices around me and a warning hurt in my leg and fur gone from the licking places. There was sleep. There was waking and weakness, many entreating noises and stroking and then there was licking time again.

Fire is comfort and runaway fear. Inside there is small fire that melts my flesh into chair contours, a rush of warmth that induces sleep and belly up stretching. It spits or crackles but it does not advance. Once, outside, it grew and hurled itself into the dark, showering the night with wild flowers of burning, exploding sudden shouts of warning. Raindrops that were not rain fell on me and seared my ears. I bolted under a shed where I suddenly smelt other cats, but the smell of fear wiped out our instinct for scratching order, and we sat quietly apart until the fire glow and noise was gone.

Food and shitting, licking time, foraging, then sleep. These are the habits with which I order the happenings of the days.

Lis Lee

OLD MAN KANGAROO

They are serving medallions of kangaroo in Glasgow.
'Darker than steak, velvety and luscious,
tenderloins of small, young kangaroo
are high in iron, low in fat'.

Back in Scotland now, I left an eye in Australia,
coveting 110 Kangaroo Ground Road, Wattle Glen,
a bungalow and four acres of grazing, ringed by bell birds
(the sound of a spoon on a half-empty milk bottle).

Kookaburras heckle daybreak.
Eucalyptus are forty shades of green,
grey, blue, silver. Leaves like coins.
Old man kangaroo, the rightful owner, coughs.
Sitting on his tail like a three-legged stool,
he is taller than the barbecue.

Gerry Loose

From: SYNCHRONICITIES

three hundred years ago the poet Basho was walking steadily
north from the capital   pausing at Sendai he met the painter
Kaemon   when they parted the artist gave the poet a pair
of sandals   a useful gift for a walker   laces dyed that exact
& unfathomed blue of an iris
about which Basho makes a poem

reading the poem   I walk from my house under blown cloud
to the Botanic Gardens   passing where Muslim sells flowers
in a tub he has iris for sale the precise colour of Basho's laces
I greet him & for less than the price of a loaf buy ten
violet flags   equal parts bruised cloud & sunshaft

we nearly did a deal on the mare & her foal at foot
after haymaking   rain starting   Tim O'Sullivan
drove off on his cabless tractor
of course he took my old duffel coat for its hood
in the tractor shed a wren built her nest in the coat pocket
& the following summer ripening
Tim rode across the bog to return it
nest eggs chicks how could he disturb her

thirty years & five floors up   on the balcony in the pot with
a clump of fern   a city pigeon has laid two
alabaster eggs   on a small clutching   of red
& yellow cut electrical wires
& I cannot go out there   even for soft spring rain

I was on fire & her cool hands quenched me
I was on fire & her hands fanned the flames

she stitched the straps of a poem to shorten it
as I put words to my silent dress

the Cubans sing on tape
what it's really like to be old

gently like mother flesh
touched & left in vacancy

bam ban and gone   into the mirror
she smoothes down her silk dress

belly, backs of thighs & waist
bam ban   a time

how today
a small redemption is given me
as the barman takes back
my untasted pint of Guinness
poured by the new barwoman
& unasked tops it
to the measure   black
after my daughter's unstated
grief had wet my
foolish eyes
& she spoke of dreams
& my cigarette burns
unheeded in the ashtray
as I write
in this bar
what is given

how we still wake in the morning
what it is you're afraid of
death perhaps, did not come &
how many comets & lunar eclipses
we miss.   my daughter sleeps now & I
smoke my last half cigarette & put
the moon back again   some ducks fly past
you there   me here   Glasgow

Irene Lotta

FREE PRESBYTERIAN DOLPHINS

i

There came a day when self-proclaiming microwaves and bargain anoraks were all that remained and we all flocked to crowded emporia to steal each other's oxygen and hide in each other's anonymity.

Pieces of plastic changed hands for an old month's salary while the lap-dancer and the bank manager jostled for places in the queue. Even a nun was seen fingering gloves tagged together by price labels worth more than the faltering goods that pronounced them to be bargains.

Gracefully then at long last I sat down. The time passed and the people passed by me. I waited. Through tiredness or pointlessness people walked slowly. I looked at the sadnesses carried by people of nine or forty-nine still wearing L-plates. Oh, how the ninety-nines mounted up, stealthily, out of their purses. Families. Lonely men. A couple in parallel talking on mobile phones not to each other. Some walking shackled in tension and others swinging loosely in the aftermath. My heart sang gratitude to the busker who alone had been able to stand still. But at last I sat down. I sat watching. In Glasgow's Argyle Street on Saturday afternoon seeing the people with nothing but money to spend.

I stood up and walked home in thin boots with heels clicking on concrete like the cloven hoof, clarity.

ii

I was born under the sea, under the glacial flood waters that seeped down to the North Sea and flooded the river mouth higher and wider than now.

When I gasped to the surface in adult life I splashed spluttered and blinked at the colours. The average colour of the universe, we are told, is a turquoisey green. That's how our life had been. We dared not depart from the norm. And so cold. And so slow if we wanted to move, like slow motion. I crawled onto the mud of the river bank and slept with my fear. When I woke I set out to find out how to live in this windswept bright world. I found that through aeons while we quietly shifted from clumsy lumpen shapes to elegant finned creatures the landlife had roared on without us at dizzying speed to evolve in much bolder ways. To make motorbikes, sports cars and helicopters, bus timetables, electric can openers, video remote controls, chat shows, trade union congresses, traffic lights. Cataloguing desperately as I went along, I crawled into the twentieth century wondering what were the odds of my survival.

Underwater we had practised elegant sharp turns, bursts of speed with the current, to escape big-teethed predators. There we had known at least which way to swim. But time passed on the land. My legs grew steadier, my clumsy grasp firmer, more agile, my skin warmer. And yet something was wrong. My new friends accepted kindness and seemed to reciprocate but always I came out the loser without knowing how. I realised that slyly they stole from me at every turn. When confronted they confessed with a smile on their faces, and then stole yet again.

On the day when I found with a shock I was contemplating how to learn the art of stealing I woke up and decided one thing must be true. The land-livers had over-evolved. They'd go on, I supposed, advancing in hellishly cleverer ways to ensure the survival of the fittest but not of the kindest. Mighty civilisation. Might, might, might be right. But not me.

I looked down at lengthening fins tinged pink with the nourishment of the blood of the few I'd outsmarted but blanched with the fear of the ones who'd devour me. I made my decision, aye, Willie, I've never regretted it much.

So one Saturday morning I scanned the horizon in silent farewell and I waded back in, ankle deep, knee deep, thigh, waist, neck, under. Back into the silence to contemplate and even sing fitfully to my brothers of the world that could some day be ours. But I doubt it. We Free Presbyterian dolphins are not born with hands we can steal with.

iii

People are eating bits of me. Yes Jesus Jeremiah Peasant Slave, it is indeed as if bones are stretched to wax, with unconsoling tears you and your misery are indeed invisible like me. I couldn't pull myself together, it engulfed me; finally some kind of faith was the decision that finally saved me in this ocean where I still swim today.

It is a half but only half submerged nightmare, a rock that crops up, some unplaceable memory between the cinema foyer and the cliff-tops, unknown, it is frightening.

For two nights I lay cold as death shivering misery, now I am burning in an excess of virulent life in my bed as I twist as if to escape thoughts and sensations of nausea.

Is it possibly safe to dive down and retrieve something now?

iv

In the town you don't hear the ocean's boom of the storm or the screaming shingle of the gale tearing through the pine trees. In the town the storm is irrelevant except for the redistribution of litter in the streets, or tiles from the roof maybe, or the destruction of cheap umbrellas. In the town we learn to be fearless as a statistic in the crowd.

My grandfather's Gaelic Bible corrupted me for all my childhood with the fear of God and towns. *Mountains, fall on us* was the cry of oh-sinner man with no-where to run to. But I knew that the hills were ages old and I had learned from the Psalms to lift my eyes to them for some kind of imaginary salvation. The only hills I could see falling on me were the mock-rococo ones of a provincial high street built to impress a four-year-old who'd never seen anything bigger than three storeys of grandeur. I was unconvinced by explanations of steel girders and pile-driven foundations. I believed an act of such audacious pride must topple and I feared to walk down the high street. Perhaps my lego house had already toppled and smashed once too often.

I sometimes go back now to see how slight those crumbling sandstone monuments to the town fathers really are. When I came back to the city last week I climbed in a glass elevator to the fourteenth floor of a new block, for a view of the dirty city I have learned affection for. I no longer know who's betrayed who in this crazy shift of values. Possibly everyone and no-one, or possibly the tragedy is that I'll never even know my own history.

v

Bottle-nosed dolphins, it's really quite rare to see them contented and playful in their own habitat chasing rainbow arcs, cousins to a shark, unbelievable that placid wide smile. How can they enjoy that icy water? Why are they always in black?

It's not my fault if they're entangled in nets meant for somebody else.

No wonder they're an endangered species.

James McGonigal

THE BLANK PAGE

Coming across a blank page
in a book of writing
like a sudden mist a clean bedsheet
or a loch reflecting November

I wondered was it deliberate tactics
on the part of the writer
like the point in a conversation
when one of us conceals our thinking

and we turn the page of the dialogue
and overleaf there are hundreds of words
to get lost in again almost forgetting
the threat and promise of that moment

and whether the absence was error or style.

LAST WEEK

The last week of your life is passing
in radio songs and cups of tea,
raindrops evaporating from rose leaves
or being sipped by the lawn.

How green the world is and unfazed
in its comings and goings.

Sometimes the rain falls straight
as the strings of a harp.
You can pick out each verse of your life
with undamaged hands.

There's still time to sort out
those holiday snaps from 1998.
Look, the final waterfall near Sligo –
a stream absolutely beside itself
with hyperventilation and rainbows.

It's started again. Fingertips of rain
find their baby nails turning pink
as freshwater pearls.

This week you may find it helpful
to greet the last few drops personally
when the lime tree by the back door
shakes them clear of its golf umbrella.

Kathy McKean

BECOMING

for my father

characters
young woman *early twenties, a gladiatrix*

location
an amphitheatre, ca 70 ad

time
summer
dawn till dusk

scene one

You think you know who I am
what I might become
you are wrong.

I will not know if it was the sun in my eyes or her blow to my
arm that will loosen my grip. I will not know if I tripped. I will
not know if it was a cloud of dust or an empire that rose and
fell at my feet.
She might know. She might tell me. I may hear.

Her breath will be on me. Hot. The heat from the hottest sun
will be swept away in the crowd's roar in the time it takes for
a drop of sweat to run from my hair down to my neck
the ground will rise
I will fall
rise and fall
her breath on me   hot
My blood will be red, bright, shining, warm. Thick like mud
the crowd will fall still
I will feel the sand. Wet and warm
she turns her head
my hand will lift, slip its grip, let me fall, close my eyes, let her
open me

the crowd will jump to its feet
wait for the signal
down
her sword will open me
show them my soul
I will hear the sounds in silence I shall follow where they lead
All this time I was chasing death when I thought he was chasing me.

scene two
Eyes on stars as I lie in wait for day. Day. Not first fight. Not torchlight. Not first –
day
Death day
Dreams grow smaller – I search for the sun – it finds me. A drop seeping through sky
a drop
from my mother's mouth down from her lip in the time it takes me to turn away my mother's face, clenched, red on white.
Turn away
I search for the sun and in its heat I feel no pain
Death
I command
Me
My mother's voice, counting stars, I learn words, names, worlds
Isis loved Osiris more than the wide world, more than the wisdom of the stars.
Osiris loved his brother Set who loved him less. Set spilt the blood he shared and Osiris was dead. Set bathed in the warmth and the wet. Tore Osiris to pieces and threw his limbs around the world.
Isis saw the red on white on the face of Osiris. Her grief was stronger than the stars that brave the sun. Isis gathered the scattered limbs and breathed his body back to life. Breathed Osiris back to life. Brought him to life to live amongst the dead.
I lie in wait for day. Not torchlight, the one light, one. All goddesses. Me.
Isis saw the red on white and breathed it back to life.
Count stars
Count deaths
I fly from death with the wings of an eagle.
Day.

scene three

Death day did not always follow me. Not follow her smile, my
laugh, his cry. Not follow with quiet eyes the silent sounds of her
death day. A thin shriek of light on a thin shriek of life. Clenched.

My mother's smile on my smile on the smile of a boy I love.
Love him running foot foot down down head back hair flying.
The smile of a boy I love.
The boy I love whispers my name. I will pass to his arms from
the arms of my father and my mother will smile at my smile
on the smile of the boy I love. Running. Foot my foot his down
mine down my hair up down up on my back.

My mother's smile.
A drop
red on white
a drop
seals her mouth
seals my smile
a drop
red on white
lies still.

I heard a song of a woman once who fought but did not see.
She could not beat them. Death dragged her away.
I beat them.
Command
I command
Death, day, Rome.

My father smiles on the smile of a man I do not love. I must
smile on him. I turn away.
My love is my smile on the smile of the boy I love. I turn away
to him. He smiles at the smile of my father. He smiles. The boy
I love whispers that I must not disobey. The boy I love tells me
I will pass from his arms to the arms of my father to the arms
of a man I do not love.
I will fight for my love. I will kill. Anything. For him. If only
he had not
asked me
to.

I do not smile. I will not be wed to a man I do not love. Not
when I love, loved the smile of another.
I will not be sold.
Not for the grave of a mother who smiles no more
I want to seal her smile, seal her red on white, seal her grave
so I will fight for her
for her I choose not to be free
Burn me, chain me, whip me, kill me
but when I fight I shall be free
take my name – give me another
give me a face of steel
bind my legs so they may be strong as trees but when I fight I
shall be free.

I fight. My father smiles. I can buy a grave for my mother. I can
buy freedom. My freedom
I smile
What is freedom worth to me?

I command emperors
I command Rome
they scream at my command.

I think of them less
I watch my memories charge out of sight as I rise and stretch
my wings
Death day
I will fly.

scene four

I am not sure if I flinch as they scan my body. One after the
other. Up and down. My eyes, straight ahead, will not meet
their gaze. They learn every inch of me. The cost of each flash
of flesh. Touch me with their eyes and.

In my head at first it is the trainers that I beat. Splintering the
wooden necks with the baton they give me. Each blow a
scream. Beat their eyes, beat their smiles, beat each flash of
flesh they see, beat my father beat my love beat that man beat
my mother NO.
Beat them

beat Rome
beat my father's law
beat Rome's law
beat their eyes
beat the sticks they brandish in front of me to see if I will flinch
Burn me beat me kill me if I disobey
burn me
beat me
kill me
if I disobey.

scene five

Head held high raise my arms
watch them light the torches, pour the scented oils
a prayer is in my head – I see my father kneeling at the shrine
close my eyes
breathe in the heat of the scent rising burning
someone kneels at my feet, takes my hand, rubs the oil, rubs
round

Torchlight. First fight. I knew what I would do
win
I would choose
My head would spin to scan the faces
every one
I would choose
I would let her head fall from my hand and I would turn and
walk away
I was wrong

Close my eyes. The scent burns. Fingers trace over my scars,
smoothing in oils, rub round.

Torchlight. My first fight
when she faced me she had no mask and I felt my own face bare
I scanned the faces. Their faces seeing mine. The smiles of men
smiling at me
they have bought me. I have sold myself to them
they laughed. I stopped them. Better. Made them scream.
Torchlight. First fight.

I could not scan each face as each face scanned my own
I could not turn away
I hold her head, her life, my choice
not them. Not by them. I would not wait for them to choose
and it was not my head spinning. Theirs. Hers. Her head twisting in my hand, them spinning with fury, rising before me,
shouting, screaming. An empire rises before me, an emperor.
My fist tight. My sword. Voices screaming yes, her head trembling no, spinning round me spinning still until the only voice
remaining is my own. And it will not be me they scream for. It
will not be my face. Clenched
red on white
I command
I do not turn away.
Lift, cut, fall. Life, blood, roar.
My foot is down on her neck before she can raise her hand
Laugh? I made them scream.

My sword cuts through the air
I stand. Victorious
My skin stiffens, tight with her blood
I look down, see her body at my feet
blood sand
brown dry and wet red
I try to slow my breath
stop, breath, in
breathe the stench out
I gag gasp
I do not know how long I can
Two hands – drag her body – away
away from my feet
blood
brown dry wet red
I gag gasp gag
please
please wash brown wet
wash wet dry

Rub round rising. They feel every muscle rub round. Feel the
heat in me. Wrap me round. My mother's hands rub round
soft. Her scent burns into me. I can see my mother's face.
Before. Not smeared with blood. She wraps me in her heat.

Wraps me warm.

The oils circle my hands circle my feet.

Feel the heat in me. Rising.

scene six

God of all worlds, all are one, Isis strengthen me
May my enemy see your face in my mask
may your hand guide my sword
blind my enemy, make her shield melt like silk
All goddesses, hear me. Isis. My own
Send death to guide my enemy
two hands drag her away
God of all worlds, all are one, Isis strengthen me
My arm be quick and strong as steel
it will be me the crowd favours, my enemy's blood they seek
my victory will be swift and strong
my hand shall rise only in battle, never in defeat
the neck of my enemy shall tilt back
my foot will stride across her soul
my sword will cut her passage to the other world
All goddesses. One. All goddesses. Me.

scene seven

I sit
tense flex tense flex
every inch of me
ready
I sit
shield on my arm, leather tight on my flesh
tense flex

My love lies in my arms lies my love and suddenly there is
someone. Suddenly there is us. My hand traces the heart of my
love, heart, heart beat, my tongue learns my love. My love lies
in my arms lies my love.

I lie on my back and see her looking, see me looking in her eyes.
She smiles and her hair falls from behind her ear down on my
cheek. Dark around me. I feel her hands on my skin, the rough
and the soft of her fingers. I learn her sounds, her shapes, how
she moves.
I wait until she sleeps so she cannot see my smile. My smile on
every line of her. Her leg by mine. My leg over her. I feel her
breathing
rise and fall

Flesh on steel, palm on steel, hot on cold
tense
hear the silence and roar of their pain
flex
my legs bound tight
hand to mask, feel the lines of my face, lines of my face, my life,
my name
flesh on steel, hot on cold, life on death

I do not tell her of me
I do not tell her of home
I do not tell her of fruits I tasted, clothes I wore, boys who
smiled at me
I do not tell her of my mother's smile nor of it frozen red on
white. I do not tell her that all I remember is that smile. I do not
tell her that I cannot be sure if that was all there was. A smile.
My mother's smile. And how little that cost

I see the eagle fly straight for me and I can't think what to feel.
It circles, swoops, away. Never mind
us
forever comes too late for us I think
in the arms of my love I will lie.

Lose
I choose
her
I choose

but

tense flex tense

scene eight

The sound and the faces merge in one angry roar
my arms raised and tense, my face, my eyes, find her
my enemy my world
this time I will lose – this fight – choose
my feet sweep the sand and I search for something in her
I do not know if I strike her or she strikes me, just feel the echo
rippling up my arm and I am falling rolling down
One breath
her beside me
one
this fight – choose
She kicks sand at my eyes
my shield flies up
I do not blink
I hear the trainer's bark as he brandishes a stick in my face and
I do not blink that time. Not because I am not afraid of the
sticks in their hands or the blades. I do not blink because I am
afraid that I might give myself – Away
turn away
blink, tears, away
I do not know if it is the tears she has seen in my eyes or the
smile
I do not ask
She sees me now
flow now
I look for something in her eyes to see the something in my own
this time I will fall
with her eyes she greets me – I cannot say if the language we
speak is hers or mine so it must be our own. From the first,
always the same
I did not speak the name they gave me and never learnt hers
arms bigger than my own. Strength stronger. She had no fear.
She did not fear me. Not fear.
I face her. Eyes. Hard
a flash of light from my sword on her shield
the crowd's roar
my mouth tight
I hear the sound she makes
my foot on her stomach
soft

she bends to my touch
I close my eyes and my sword catches the light that blinds her.
I lie on my back and see her looking, see me looking in her eyes.
I feel her breathing
rise
fall
her stomach soft by mine
her head on my arm, her head in my hand. Rise and fall
and her I will not harm
her I will not kill
for
rise and fall
I cannot be at peace unless she is
I kneel breathless at her feet
I want to raise my hand, tilt my head back, let her open, let her
spill, let her – kill – me
but first her eyes
I want her to know what I have been chasing what I have found
she squints and I cannot see
shield her eyes her shield crashes down
she thinks she can
I cannot see
she thinks she can beat me, bind me
her eyes
she thinks she can break me
her eyes that do not hold me
she thinks she can watch me fall
my sword lifts
my grip slips
I fall
still
I fall
I look up and see her, see her looking. Not looking. See her
sword.
Arms bigger than my own. Strength stronger. Not fear. Me.
Not fear.
She thinks she knows who I am. What I might become. She is
wrong

My hand finds my sword once more
flesh on steel
hot on cold
life or death
choose
I choose
her
I choose her
I meet her eyes
break her sword
force her down
she kneels at my feet
her head in my hand
her hair
soft
wet
my blade at her neck
I say her name
close my eyes
her head
her breath
her sweat
I turn the blade flat and feel her pulse echo through me
close my eyes
Cut   Blood   Fall
Smile   Blood   Roar

For a moment it is not real
body, feet, me
at her feet
for a moment it is all as I saw, all as I felt
love
I have lost
I stand
Victorious
body, feet, her body, my feet
alone.
A whole world's fury in my ears
red sky shining
I wait
for waters to flood, wash away blood, her blood to wash my feet
two hands drag

a cloud of dust and an empire falls at my feet - my feet
the sun dries her blood to my skin
I can see her face, her mouth, open
I can see me in her eyes
I can feel her hair fall soft on my face
I can feel her shape underneath me
how it moves, moulds into my own
her hands drag blood across the sand
Tell me what is this thing I am and how do I get back to me?
The sky is pink with anger and I fall
a whole world moves around me and I fall
I fall
I fall and the sky is pink with anger and I fall.

You think you know who I am
What I might become

David S. Mackenzie

GILFEDDER

Gilfedder said: *It's not easy with a sore stomach.*
It's what? I said.
Difficult, he said, *difficult to lift a crate when you've a sore stomach.* And then he punched me hard in the solar plexus. I doubled over and fell to my knees. My eyes watered and I gasped like a wheezy old bellows.
Gilfedder leaned over and spoke to me quietly, in my ear: *I run this place, right? And I don't like fancy cunts like you. Right? This is a man's job, this, so you've no fuckin' chance.* Then he straightened up and walked away.
I managed to pull myself up and sit on a chair. I leaned forward and spread myself across the formica-topped table, one of three in the empty staff room. I lay like this for a full minute, trying to regulate my breathing. Then I sat up. My stomach hurt like hell. I wasn't sure I could even stand, far less lift a crate of fish. But I did stand up. I picked up my red rubber gloves from the table and stumbled towards the door. I steadied myself against the wall as I made my way slowly along the corridor that led to the loading bay.
I held myself pretty much erect as I walked across the floor to join the other men who were already starting to unload the lorry that had drawn up alongside the bay. Each wooden crate of fish was grabbed by two men, one each end, and swung down from the lorry onto a pallet made of thick slats of pine. A couple of men stood on the lorry itself and shifted the crates into position for the unloaders. The whole place was cold and everything smelled of fish.
Morgan, the night shift leader, said: *Gilfedder, you work with the new man.*
I'm no workin' with that, Gilfedder said, without looking round. He had decided to lift the crates by himself and he did so with ease, taking hold of them as if they were empty and flinging them down on the pallets. Lumps of ice from the crates scattered across the floor of the loading bay. *Mind and no spill any,* Morgan said but Gilfedder gave no indication he'd heard. To me Morgan said: *Up on the lorry, then, and give Bob and the Mule a hand.* I did as I was bidden.
Of course Gilfedder was right: it was very difficult for me

to lift the crates when my stomach ached so much. I started slowly, got slower still but managed to recover later on.

The bed of the lorry and the stone floor of the loading bay were the same height so when only a couple of layers of crates remained on the lorry we were no longer dropping crates down onto the pallets, we were building the pallets up. Most of the men were now on the lorry. I found myself next to Gilfedder. *How's the new cunt?* he said to me. *Oh fine,* I replied. I managed to pick up a crate by myself and I flung it up onto the rising levels of the nearest pallet. A herring slipped out and landed at my feet. *Mind and no spill any, new cunt,* Gilfedder said. I picked up the herring and flung it into the nearest crate.

When the lorry was unloaded we trooped through to the freezing room. It was as if we were still outside. The freezing room was a huge hall with a high ceiling and it was filled with cold air, the stink of fish and the loud purring of the motors that powered the freezing vats. Bob and the Mule had left their early job on the lorry and had moved the fully laden pallets through from the loading bay using forklift trucks. The pallets were now lined up next to the freezing vats.

Morgan said: *Right, let's fill the bastards.*

Again, we worked in pairs, emptying the crates into the vats. We had to spread the fish carefully so that they slipped down between the vertical metal plates inside the vats. These plates were about four inches apart. When each vat was full of fish they were all sprayed with water until the vats held only vertical slices four inches thick and made out of water and tightly packed fish. Then the freezing began. Within half an hour the fish were frozen into slabs. The slabs were then pushed up from below until they stuck up above the vats and could be snapped off, stacked on pallets and driven round to the cold room for storage.

It took fifteen minutes or so to fill all seven vats with fish and thirty minutes for the vats to freeze completely. This meant that when we had finished filling the vats we had about fifteen minutes to wait until the first vat was ready for emptying. Assuming there wasn't another lorry to be unloaded, we could have a break. We went back through to the staff room.

This was a small room completely without adornment. The yellow walls were bare. The pale blue tops of the formica tables were stained with odd spots and rings of tea and coffee and spilled cigarette ash. There were fifteen chairs made of tubular metal and with plastic seats and backs. The two ceiling lights were extremely bright as if to convince us we were working during the day, not at night. The place stank of cigarettes and fish. The men took off their dark red rubber aprons and flung them on the backs of the chairs. They took out their piece boxes from their haversacks and ate their sandwiches. They drank from thermos flasks. When they'd eaten and drunk they got out their roll-up tins and made cigarettes whose smoke rose, gathered and settled in a layer just above head height. There was little conversation apart from speculation as to the arrival time of the next lorry. Then Gilfedder said, loudly, so that no one could miss him: *How's the new boy doin'?*

Oh, just fine, I said. *Just fine.*

Stomach OK?

Never better.

Then the Mule, who was a man in his early sixties, said to Gilfedder: *Leave the lad alone, Donnie. He'll be just grand if you let him be.*

Keep out o' this, Mule, Gilfedder said. *If he's a lad then he shouldna be here. This is man's work.*

I looked at Gilfedder properly for the first time. I guessed he was about thirty years old. He was quite a big man – about six feet tall – and very broad. Although the same height as me he must have been a couple of stones heavier and none of this was fat. He was physically fit and robust but his face betrayed him, displaying to those who could read it, the mixture of strengths and weaknesses afforded by his physique. For he had a look that bordered on desperation, as if it was necessary for him to assert his physical superiority moment by moment. And his expression made me feel that if this confirmation were denied him then something inside him might fragment with consequences that were unpredictable but almost certainly bad.

Man's work, he said again, looking across at me. *This is fucking man's work.*

I knew I had to say something but invention left me. I was glad that Morgan came in to announce the arrival of the next lorry. Piece boxes were closed, thermoses capped and aprons were tied on again. We went back out to the loading bay.

The night shift finished at eight o'clock, just as it was beginning to get light. Someone had let down the tyres on my bike. Gilfedder, I supposed. At least he hadn't slashed them. I pumped them up and then cycled home.

• • •

I didn't sleep much that day for thinking about the job and Gilfedder and wondering if I could survive either. I decided to build myself a breastplate made of tin with long thin sharp nails protruding on one side. I would goad Gilfedder into hitting me in the stomach again and watch him scream in agony as he smashed his knuckles into the needle-like points of the nails.

Because I wanted to hurt Gilfedder; I wanted to hurt him very much indeed. It didn't matter to me if he was off work for weeks and then lost his job. I couldn't understand how someone so evil could exist at all. He was a bad man and I wanted to hurt him badly. With this vengeance in mind I managed to fall asleep for a couple of hours. When I woke up I felt more tired than before and my stomach hurt where Gilfedder had punched me. And I was depressed. My breastplate of nails idea was ridiculous. Any type of retaliation was silly. Escalation of conflict. I could see a future of knuckle-dusters and baseball bats, maybe even knives. When it came to violence Gilfedder was an expert; I was a rank amateur. I decided that the only way I might overcome him would be to take everything he dished out and respond only with silence. After a while he would get bored with the whole enterprise. It wasn't much of a strategy but it was the only one I had.

At the beginning of the next shift he slapped me on the back. Hard. *Come back for more, eh, new cunt? I thought you'd have more sense, educated bastard like you.* I turned and looked at him but said nothing. *No speakin', eh?* He smiled at me. I walked out into the loading bay. We started on the first lorry. As usual Gilfedder worked alone. I started off working with the Mule. At one point Morgan left the loading bay and went into the freezing room to check the vats. I heard Gilfedder shout: *Hey, new cunt, catch!* I turned to see something flying towards me. Instinctively I put my hands up to my face and this thing thudded into them. It was a dogfish. They often turned up among the herring. They were strange creatures, long and thin like stretched out sharks. When you dipped your hands into the herring boxes you had to be careful because dogfish have a long sharp spike that sticks up at the trailing edge of the dorsal fin. Sometimes you knew you'd found a dogfish only when this spur hit you, went through your glove and into your hand. The cut could be deep and painful. As it was on this occasion because it was the back of the fish that hit my palms and the spur entered my hand at the base of my right thumb. I doubled up in pain. There was a lot of laughter, all from the one man.

He's a bugger, that man, the Mule said to me quietly as he inspected my hand which was oozing blood. *Just go through to the office and ask for the first aid box.*

I did as he suggested. Gilfedder watched me go and laughed some more. When I got back, having dabbed the wound with antiseptic and stuck a plaster on it, I said nothing to anyone. I got a fresh pair of gloves from the store and carried on working. *Well!* Gilfedder said loudly, as usual. *Second shift and already got through your first pair of gloves. What a hard worker we've got here, eh?* I ignored him.

In the morning, at the end of the shift, my tyres were flat again. This time they had been slashed. I wheeled the bike home. I slept for four hours and dreamed of herring. I was in the sea with them, shoals of them swimming round me, and I was trying to catch them. I was wearing a pair of enormous red gloves and perhaps my hands, too, were enormous inside them. I reached out and tried to snatch the fish as they swam past. I didn't catch any. I got up and wheeled the bike into town. I got new tyres and inner tubes and cycled back. At seven thirty I cycled to work for the start of my third shift.

Hey, how's the bike? Gilfedder asked me when I walked into the staff room. I ignored him but I sat down at the same table he was sitting at. There was no one else at that table. *I said how's the bike?* Gilfedder repeated, but I said nothing. I took my piece box from my bag and put it on the table. *I fuckin' asked you a question,* Gilfedder said and his tone had moved from derision to menace. I continued to ignore him. A hand reached over and swiped the piece box from in front of me. Luckily the lid was still on. It landed on the floor by the door, right at the feet of Morgan who was just stepping in. Bewildered, Morgan picked it up. *Whose is this?* he asked. I stood up. *Mine,* I said and I took it from him. *Lorry's in,* Morgan said and we all went out to the loading bay.

Gilfedder's big joke on that third night was to fill my piece box with herring guts. He laughed when I opened the box and found my sandwiches inedible but I said nothing. I knew I'd be very hungry but I still said nothing. I drank my tea in silence. I carefully sniffed the tea first, believing that he might have pissed in it but he hadn't. Maybe he was saving that for the next night. *Eat your sandwiches, why don't you, eh?* he said. I continued to ignore him. *Hey, new cunt, I'm talkin' to you. I'm fuckin' talkin' to you.* He leaned over the table.

I knew the next thing would be a hand swiping at my mug, and I was right. I just moved the mug back out of Gilfedder's reach and he missed. Not only that but in trying to deliver the blow he'd overstretched himself and he lost his footing on the slippery tiles of the floor. He tumbled over, catching his side on the corner of the table and he landed on the floor in a heap. Everyone in the staff room, except me, burst out laughing. I carried on drinking my tea.

As he got up from the floor Gilfedder winced very slightly, just enough to show that he had done himself some damage as he fell.

But when he managed to stand up, leaning on the table for support, he was more enraged than before. *Which o' you cunts was laughin' at me!* he screamed at us. I wanted to say: *Everyone*, but I didn't. The Mule said it for me.

We all laughed, ye daft gowk, he said. *You fair excelled yourself there.*

I'll brain any man that laughs at me, Gilfedder shouted.

Well, you'll just have to wipe out the entire gang o' us then, the Mule went on in his usual quietly amused fashion. *Which is fine if you fancy unloading all those lorries just by yourself.*

Gilfedder stood there for a few moments without saying anything. He was full of anger which hadn't yet found a way out. He turned to look at me. I knew he was looking at me because he seemed to be turned in my direction but I was not looking at him. This was part of my plan. I would never talk to him and never look at him. But I knew he was looking at me. I was nearest, just across the table. He could easily hit me now; there was nothing to stop him. I expected him to hit me. I might try to move away but I would not retaliate. I would not retaliate because that's what he wanted me to do. I sipped my tea and waited for the blow.

But he didn't hit me. He just pointed at me. He pointed at me and said: *I'll fix you, you cunt. I'll fuckin' fix you.*

Now he was a little boy in the playground, reduced to making threats. I decided I was winning.

During the course of the next hour it became clear that Gilfedder was struggling. He continued to work alone when unloading the lorries but the fluency with which he plucked the crates from the stack and flung them down on the pallets was not there any more. He began to keep his right arm tucked close in to his body so that he looked lopsided and awkward. The other men noticed this too. I could see nods in Gilfedder's direction and I heard them muttering that it served the bastard right.

By six in the morning when the fifth lorry of the night arrived Gilfedder was still working alone but he was moving slowly. He was clearly in pain. I tried to feel sorry for him but I couldn't. Morgan came over to me and said: *Give Gilfedder a hand, will you, Tom.* The nearest men paused in their work and looked over at the two of us. Gilfedder was standing to one side, breathing heavily. I wasn't sure if he'd heard Morgan's request but I made sure he heard my reply. I said: *I'm not working with that.* I rejoined the Mule and we worked together till the end of the shift. No one spoke to Gilfedder. Everyone left him to work at his own pace which became slower and slower. During the breaks he sat at the same table as me in the staff room but he said nothing to anyone. At seven o'clock Morgan said to him: *Why don't you go home if you're in pain?* And someone added, quietly: *Aye, and fuckin' stay there for the rest of your life.* But Gilfedder shook his head. He was determined to make it to the end of the shift. And he did.

But he didn't turn up for work the following evening. *Cracked rib,* Morgan reported when someone finally got round to asking, during the first break. *He'll be off for a while, too. Great shame, he's a good man.*

Define 'good', the Mule asked but Morgan didn't reply.

Someone else said: *How long's a while?*

Morgan thought for a moment. *Signed off for a month, I think,* he said.

Could you not make it two?

Morgan looked at the man who had spoken. The rest of the men laughed. *So what's wrong with Gilfedder, then?* Morgan asked.

What's right wi' him, more like, the Mule said.

Well, he works hard, Morgan replied.

Does he work any harder than any of the rest of us? the Mule countered.

Morgan looked round the assembled men. After a silence

that lasted too long, he said: *Well, no, I wouldn't say that, no.* A few moments later he left the room.

Then the Mule said: *Daft or what? If Gilfedder's the biggest bastard in the world, then Morgan's the daftest. Canna see what's starin' him in the face.*

But when you think of him workin' wi' a cracked rib, Morrison said.

What?

Gilfedder, workin' wi' a cracked rib.

So?

Well, I'm just sayin'…pride, I don't know…

Well, the Mule went on, *it's not pride if you ask me, it's his damn hard head. You're not takin' his side now, are you?*

No, no. I'm just sayin'…

Just sayin' what?

Well, that you've got to hand it to him, that's all…

Hand it to him? By God I'd fuckin' hand it to him. You're beginning to sound like Morgan.

And at that point Morgan returned and announced that the fish were now frozen and it was time to get them out and stacked.

While Gilfedder was away, things were so much easier. I even began to enjoy the work. The fact that Gilfedder would inevitably return was a threat, of course, but not for the first week, at least. I got to know some of the men and I began to learn from them about how to work more efficiently – how not to tire myself out in the first couple of hours of my shift. They taught me by example a number of things which were apparently very simple but also very useful. I learned the correct way to lift a box of fish so that I didn't expend too much energy. If I needed to lift it two feet then that was precisely how far I should lift it. Not three feet or even two feet and an inch. Just two feet. *Push and slide as much as possible,* the Mule told me. *And when you're lifting, use your legs as much as possible. Don't lean over. Bend your legs then straighten. They're stronger than your arms, after all. And don't charge at the work. It's a long race this, not a sprint.*

So what about Gilfedder? I asked him.

What about him?

All this business about not charging at the work. That's exactly what he does.

The Mule shook his head. *You're right,* he said. *You're right.*

*Don't know where he gets the energy from. So much fuckin'
energy he canna keep it in.*

Mostly it was my doing but often the talk came back to
Gilfedder. I learned a lot about him, or rather, I learned a lot
about what people believed of him. And there were many
contradictions. Morrison swore on his life that Gilfedder's
father had been a miner and had died in a pit accident when
Gilfedder was eight years old. But Bob had met a cousin of
Gilfedder's when he was on a construction job in Aberdeen and
he'd said that Gilfedder's father had been in the Army and had
died in a car accident up in Caithness, somewhere near Halkirk.

One of the men had been at school with Gilfedder but even
he seemed unsure about the facts. Gilfedder had been suspended
from school several times but he couldn't bring to mind the
details of any of Gilfedder's offences. Certainly Gilfedder had
played football for the school and he'd even had a trial for a
team in one of the Scottish divisions – Motherwell, he thought.
Morrison said no, it was definitely Celtic but everyone laughed
at this. Anyway, all were agreed that whichever team was
involved nothing had come of it. Like most of his classmates at
school, Gilfedder had wound up in a succession of labouring
jobs. This was his second stint at the fish factory. He'd spent a
year here about three years ago but left for a better job on a
construction site on the West Coast. When that job ended he'd
come back and been rehired here straight away.

They like him because he works hard, the Mule said, shaking his head.

Well, he does work hard, doesn't he? Morrison offered.

Would you employ him then?

Well, no, I wouldn't.

And why not?

Well, he's…

He's no right in the head, the Mule said. *Clean daft and
dangerous with it. Should be in Nain House, if you ask me.*

He's been there, Morrison said.

What?

He's been there. Twice that I know of.

Now he tells us.

What happened? I asked.

Oh, it was a while ago now, Morrison said.

A while ago? the Mule asked.

Years ago. Ancient history.

So?

So what?

So why did they put him in there? the Mule asked.

Yes. What happened? I repeated.

It was clear that Morrison now regretted having mentioned the issue. *I'm no sayin' nothing more*, he said, but then added: *He wasnae long out of school. A long time ago. All forgotten now.*

You haven't forgotten it, the Mule said. *And I'm damn sure Gilfedder hasn't forgotten it.*

It's nothing, Morrison said. *It's... I shouldna have mentioned it at all.*

Damn right you shouldna have mentioned it, Bob said. *I imagine Gilfedder'll no be too pleased either.*

Don't none of you fuckin' mention this to him, Morrison said. *Not a fuckin' word.* For a moment he looked genuinely scared.

Just tell us why, the Mule said. *Just tell us why he was in there. We'll no say a word. None of us.* There were murmurs of approval from round the room. *Come on.*

Morrison looked at us. He looked over at the men sitting at the other tables. *Not a fuckin' word, right?*

We all agreed to this. *Not a word. Don't worry. Nothing. Not a word.*

Morrison looked down at the open sandwich box in front of him. *Depression*, he said. *Tried to kill himself.*

Someone said: *No!* in a voice of quiet surprise. Then there was a short silence until the Mule said: *Twice?*

Morrison nodded. *Twice.*

Someone said: *Poor bastard. Would you believe it? Poor bastard.*

Someone else said: *Poor bastard my arse. Two chances to be rid of the bugger and neither of them came off.*

Gilfedder may have been signed off for a month as Morgan had suggested but he was back within two weeks. He was first in the staff room at the beginning of the shift, sitting at his usual table. He winked at me when I came in and he must have noticed the surprise on my face, though I said nothing. I sat down and emptied my haversack as usual and I didn't say anything. Nor did he say anything to me but I knew he was looking at me. As the men trooped in there were a lot of surprised faces. *So soon?*

someone said, and someone else said: *Aye, Donnie, how's the ribs, eh?* But he said nothing in reply, nothing at all. He spoke to no one and this was new and it made me afraid.

When we got to the loading bay to tackle the first lorry of the night, Gilfedder tore into the stacks of boxes as if his two week absence had been for special training rather than convalescence. His work rate through the first two hours of the shift was so high that even Morgan found it hard to believe. *Will you look at that,* he said to no one in particular. *God almighty, what's that man on?* The Mule said: *Diesel, most like. Gives you a fair boost, eh?*

Gillfedder's huge energy and drive depressed me because his injury had obviously not slowed him down at all, nor subdued him in the slightest. And his silence was unnerving. It didn't strike me until much later that he might be using the same tactics as me. But whereas my silence was that of feigned indifference, his was all about the creation of menace.

At the end of the first break, during which he didn't say a word to anyone, he was one of the last to leave the staff room. I stayed until he'd been gone perhaps half a minute before I too set off back to the loading bay. But he was waiting for me in the corridor. And he spoke for the first time that night.

Well, well, he said to me. *You're still here, eh?*

I said nothing and made to pass him. He grabbed me by the lapels. *Just a wee word, that's all,* he said, his face so close to mine that I could feel his breath on my face. I could smell it, too – the sour smell of cigarettes.

Just fuckin' watch it, that's all.

I turned my head to one side so that I wasn't looking at him. I was determined to continue to ignore him, to put up with whatever he did to me. I still believed that my will was stronger than his, that he would be worn down before I was. But I also knew that ignoring him only provoked him to greater anger and violence. I heard him say: *How's the stomach?* He released me and I braced myself for the blow which duly arrived. He hit me so hard that I was flung backwards, folded up like paper. I wound up sitting on the cold black and white floor tiles. I turned round to spew up the egg sandwich I'd just eaten and found myself on my hands and knees like a sick dog, back arching as I continued to vomit up my food.

When I'd finished retching I sat on the floor again, leaning back against the wall with my knees up close to my chest.

Gilfedder had gone and I hadn't noticed his going nor even what his parting comment might have been. I managed to pull a handkerchief from my pocket and wipe my mouth. I sat there for some minutes and I knew I was completely beaten. The idea that I could somehow wear Gilfedder down seemed laughable. What was I trying to do? – allow myself to be punched so often that eventually he broke his knuckles? My plan was ridiculous, farcical. My stomach ached. I stayed sitting on the floor inhaling from my clothes the smell of herring and puked-up egg sandwiches. I decided that I would get up, clean up the mess in the corridor and go home. After all, what did it matter? I was placing Gilfedder at the centre of my life, moulding my life round my fixation with him. Why continue to do this? I could just walk away. There were other jobs; there were lots of other jobs. I got to my feet. It was difficult to straighten up properly and I leaned against the wall for support. My stomach would hurt for a couple of days, maybe more, but then it would wear off and I wouldn't be here anyway. I would be somewhere else, no longer interested in Gilfedder or herring or working twelve hour shifts in a huge shed full of cold air.

I found a mop and bucket and was just finishing cleaning up the mess when the Mule arrived. *What's up wi' you then?* he asked.

Nothing, I said.

Nothing? He looked at me. *Morgan sent me.*

Did he?

Aye. It was Gilfedder said something to him.

Did he now. And what did he say?

Said you were sick or something.

Well, I was.

Were you?

Something in the sandwich.

Your piece?

Yes.

The Mule took hold of the mop and stopped me from finishing my task. *Gilfedder thumped you, didn't he?*

No, I said, *he didn't.*

The Mule took the mop and bucket from me. *I'll put these away,* he said. *And don't think you're the only one Gilfedder's thumped in the gut.*

He's never hit you, has he? I asked.

Aye, once, the bastard. But he'll no do it again. Reckons

I'm too old, I imagine.

I stepped up to the Mule and took hold of the handle of the mop, partly to steady myself, partly to get close. *You're kidding,* I said. *He hit you? He actually hit you?*

Just the once. As I say, a while ago now.

God almighty, I said. *And you're apologising for him, too. Jesus Christ, I don't believe it.*

He's a sly one, the Mule went on. *Aye, he's thumped one or two of us but there's never any witnesses, like. If he gets you on your own there's no much you can do... I mean, either to prevent it or to do anything about it later.*

Jesus, I said. *Jesus Christ.*

I stepped away, leaned against the wall. I looked at the Mule and wondered if that would be me in thirty years' time.

The Mule said: *Are you going home then?*

No, I said, *I'm not.*

It'll likely get worse.

Likely it will, I said.

We went back to the loading bay. The men were nearly half-way through the next lorry. The first full pallet was being driven off to the freezing room. A thin fog, made up of the men's breath and the vapour rising from the ice packed in the fish boxes, enclosed the men. It spread from the loading bay itself out over the open back of the lorry where Bob and Morrison were still working, shifting crates to the lorry's edge.

Morgan looked at me as I approached. *You OK?* he asked.

Fine, I said. *Fucking sandwich came back on me.* I looked inside the nearest fish box. *What's this? Mackerel?*

Aye, mackerel, Morgan said. *We get them occasionally. Fat little buggers. Have to push them down hard between the slats.*

Yeah?

Yeah. Don't know why we bother.

Right, I said. *Anyway, I'd better get on. I'll take a turn with Gilfedder.*

You'll what?

But I was already away, walking over to where Gilfedder was working, as usual, alone. He didn't notice me as I came up to him.

Come on, Gilfedder, let me give you a hand there, I said.

He turned to look at me. For a moment he was surprised, then he laughed. *You?* he said. *You give me a hand? You're joking.*

No, I said, sounding as breezy as I could manage. *I'd like to give you a hand tonight.*

Well you can just fuck off. He grabbed another crate from the lorry and swung it down onto the pallet.

No, no. Look, I said. *You've just come back after cracking a rib. I mean, you should take it easy, that's all.*

He already had the next crate in his hands, the heavy red gloves tight round the wet wooden handles. He stopped in mid-swing and looked hard at me. Instead of putting the crate onto the pallet he threw it down at his feet on the stone floor of the loading bay. The impact made the contents recoil upwards. Some of the ice spilled out and one mackerel slipped from the box and fell down between the lorry and the edge of the loading bay.

What the fuck are you talking about?

Everybody stopped work and watched us. I spoke confidently, loudly, so that they could all hear. *I'm just saying,* I said, *that you should let someone help you when you're maybe not quite up to it.*

Not up to it? He looked at me first in bewilderment and then in anger. *Not up to it?* He stepped over the fish box he had just flung down and screamed *Fuck off!* at me. He lunged forward and pushed me back, the heels of his hands thumping into my chest. I lost my balance and fell down, clattering into the half-built pallet behind me. But I scrambled back up again as quickly as I could. Morgan, hovering somewhere to my right, was saying: *Now hold on, Donnie, just hold on...* But neither he nor anyone else came near us.

I stepped back up to Gilfedder and said: *But you don't understand, do you? You're a sick man, Gilfedder. You need help. You can't manage on your own.*

I turned away just enough to reduce the full power of the punch. I wanted a bruise, not a broken jaw. But nothing could have prepared me for the explosion of force on the side of my head. It was as if someone had hit me with a fence post. Perhaps only a few seconds passed before I became aware that I was lying on my right side on the floor. My right arm was flung out above my head along the cold wet stone. I could feel dampness seeping through my clothes and reaching my skin. There was a great deal of noise, lots of shouting and running around, it seemed. I could see, before my face, some ice and a couple of mackerel, the deep blue-green sheen on their backs, the thin points of their tails, and I found myself thinking about how big they were, huge in fact, and Morgan was right when he said they wouldn't fit between the freezing plates in the vats. I lay there for some time or perhaps only a few seconds. My face slowly tilted to the floor and my nose became wet. Then I tasted stone and water and fishblood and the oil from the mackerel that scummed the surface of the shallow puddles and invaded the crushed ice that had been scattered across the floor of the loading bay.

Kirsten McKenzie

FIVE WINTER HAIKU

Through the window
A bird's piercing note
In the dark

Deep grey sky
Steady swish
Of passing cars

Thin powder snow
My foot slips
Into brown slush

Deer prints in the snow
And an animal
With only one leg

Little clouds of steam
At the bus stop
This morning

Rob Mackenzie

DESIGNER BIRTHDAY FOR LITTLE BROTHER

Fair Trade Family's son talk Adidas
And only Adidas must do.

Try you flirt from Oxfam shirt?
Dance slow blue in Traidcraft shoe?

Don't like cause no fuss
But only designer will does.

So ain't no one not pay
Little brother's big day?

Not mama, she bulk buying
Organic bananas,

Not papa, he futon lying
In recycled pyjamas,

Not sister, by whisker saving
Last existing pandas;

Each living by causes,
Their should be's and was's,

The will and the possible,
The likely that won't.

So he stole him Adidas
For only Adidas would don't.

Cathy Mary MacMillan

LUATH AIR A CHAGAILT

Mar luath fuar 'sa mhadainn
'n deidh teas teine na h- oidhche,
mo bheatha na laighe,
sgaipt' air cagailt mo chuimhn'.

Gach bliadhna chaidh seachad,
bha dòchas is gràdh
a fàs is a' neartachadh
mo spiorad is mo dhàìmh,
mo chreidimh a' daighneachadh
ann an Dia nan dùl,
thug dhomhsa 's mi neo-airidh
gach maitheas bho laimh.

O Eubha co chuireadh caire ort
fhear mhillidh nan gràìnn
cho seòlta gam mhealladh
gu maireadh gu bràth,
mo shuaimhneas, mo thaitneas
mo chèile le ghràdh,
cho dìleas, cho maireann
gu deireadh mo lò.

Mo theaghlach mum chasan
ri mo chridhe cho dlùth,
's am beatha na spealgan
le cealgaireachd a' bhrùìd,
thanaig ann an sàmhla fear teaghlaich
g'ar mealladh le mùirn.

An oidhche dubh, dorch le dòrainn
gun phriobhadh chadail na'm shùil
mi glàòdh ri mo Shlànuighear
gun mo threigsinn gu tur.
Ach tha mhadainn ag imeachd
gun mhaill is gun thruais
's an luath fhathast air a' chagailt
's i ri sgapadh ris a' ghaoith.

Mo bheatha na fheallsanachd
mo dhòchas na smùr
m'anam na fhàsach
gun foillseachadh dùil,
mo chridhe gun aire
gu bheil buille fhathast na'm chòm,
's gur fheudar dhomh bhith maireann,
le'm chràidh gu deireadh tìm.

ASHES ON THE HEARTH

As the cold ashes of the morning
from the night's red hot fire,
so my life lies scattered
across the hearth stone of my mind.

As the years walked on
hope and love grew
drew my spirit and heart
to new strengths in faith
in the Lord of all,
who gave me, undeserving
all good by His hand.

O Eve who would blame you
the wretched spoiler's
deceitful lies
Promising happiness everlasting
Peace and joy
a loving, faithful husband
till end of Days.

My children around me
so dear to my heart
their lives in shattered splinters
The beast came in guise of a father
to lie with love, intent.

The night long, dark, in sorrow
with no sleep in my eye
calling sore to my Saviour
don't ever desert
But morning is creeping
pitiless and sure
Ashes still to be scattered
to the wild wind.

My life a philosophy
my hope in dust
my soul a desert
no revelation in sight
my heart still aware
of the beat within
that I must live with this grief
till the end of my days.

Hugh McMillan

A GUIDE TO DUMFRIES

That's the Nith,
and that's a herring gull.
There's a man asleep on a bench
beside a herring gull.
There are two alkies
and a herring gull,
isn't that nice?
Now that's a black headed –
no sorry, there was a chip bag in the way –
it's a herring gull.
There's the open top bus tour
with Michael Sullivan showing his arse off the back,
over there by the kebab shop
and those herring gulls.
And here's some drunk Geordies throwing
beer cans at the swan,
because the herring gulls are too fast.
Do you know herring gulls
can hang on thermals
high enough to lose sight of the slack faces,
the boarded up shop fronts,
and garlands of sick,
and see just a patchwork of water,
earth and stone,
the original plan?
Herring gulls can *do* that.
They're a menace.

Andrew McNeil

YOU KNOW

You know
Like when it is a day's end
Like the speed of the day
Calling on strength years away
How the workload weighs
Ambition's poison line-managed down.

You know how
Small pieces are eaten
The mountain of paper remains
Targets for the targets
Throughput drilled in bone marrow

You know
The desperate calm
In skin-lines of those in power
For power's sake

You know how it is
When the kids' days
Come last not first

You know that kind of day

Well, here was my heart
Dissected out in short measure
Bloody and moist on my palm

The kestrel had given it back
A gift spied from my car
Poised in precision lines
The hill fort
The Iron Age remains
The bird
Green below hiding
Whatever other prey
She seeks

You know it
That kind of Fife scene.

Andy Manders

THE LAST FERRY BEFORE THE SABBATH

for Ranald

if i could go back anywhere it'd be the thought of two more
nights in a wet tent on harris washing across your face like the
rain that looks like it doesn't clearing for the first time in a
generation to let the lift we knocked back from callanish come
up on deck to wave it'd be the rain and how quick it comes
back it'd be the rain and the sound of the rain on one fly-sheet
flapping in the middle of nowhere on what was probably your
side it'd be the rain and the role of the rain in the all-night
cheese versus tobacco when the shop opens first thing monday
morning debate it'd be the rain and mair bloody rain and no
end to the rain till aesthetics prevail and every last crossing o
every last journey o every last last gets rained fucking aff – and
we sit opposites abandoned drookit on a bridge across aw the
roads we walked thegither listening out for breaks in the rain

Irfan Merchant

FURNITURE

I like to read, of an afternoon,
in the café in the main hall
of the Royal Museum. I sit
at my usual table, at the edge
beside the low blond-wood partition,
sheltered by a tall pot-plant.
From here, I see all; who comes, who goes.
I have my usual: some books,
a pen, a notepad, a double espresso;
my hat on my bag on the chair beside me.

I'd like to think it has good *feng shui* –
plenty of space under the glass roof
for the *chi* to flow, a central fishpond,
three bronze Buddhas, round tables,
and the plants – but I can't be sure
as my knowledge is limited to a leaf
through *Feng Shui For Modern Living*
while waiting in The Curry Connection.
This much I can say: air and light,
and the tiled floor white as this page.

I'll stir the coffee, take some notes.
The clock ticks in its tabernacle.
Perhaps you'll see me here, one day,
at about three. I look like *Saint Jerome
in his Study*. In my Museum,
around the corner, stuffed, symmetrical
as Antonello's painting, an eagle
and a peacock; a dozing tabby cat;
and a lion, paw raised, creeping towards me
but moving no closer, and no further away.

MERCURY

When the filling my father (a dentist) once filled
fell out of its molar, I staved off toothache
for months, with a mixture of clove oil and whisky.
This self-treatment might've been folly but worked
till the night I lay sleepless in Barcelona,
the pain swelling like a balloon in my skull.
In a stupor, I sweated it out on the balcony;
watched the sky darken, until it bleached white.
I had to do something. The dentist I found
up a winding stone stair, in a cavernous room
was much more an old alchemist who could tell
from my gestures: *El diente esta muerto.*
(Dead?! I'd not realised teeth have their *own* lives;
like tiny white molluscs they cling to the cave-walls,
the tongue a red eel coiled within the lagoon…)
Prescribing a sachet of Ibuprofen,
he counselled me to see my own dentist soon.
I gulped the solution like magical potion.

The short story is: a flight back to Edinburgh,
a young dentist dredging canals like a hero
preserving the tooth-bed from further erosion.
That tooth now a relic, a memento mori,
a tombstone, a curio, as well as a corpse;
the shell living on long after the dweller
by virtue of some non-mercurial substance
for which I paid handsomely. By this operation
are lost roots redeemed, the grit in the oyster
transformed to a pearl, the pearl of great price.

Marion F. Morrison

BEANNAICH AR LAITHEAN SAORA –
O CAUSA NOSTRA LAETITIAE*

An latha mu dheireadh den sgoil
An laoidh mu dheireadh den term
Maquisards a' ghlinne
A' cluich aig Cosa Nostra
Saoghal Al Capone –
Na leig ort neo tha thu marbh!!

A' tachairt aig na pòlaichean
Le falach fead, dresser beag
Cogadh ùr gach latha,
The Bay of Pigs, neo
Co 's fheàrr? Na Barraich
Neo na h- Uibhistich?

Ruith mi le mo chearcal
A gliongadaich sios an rathad
Cho luath ri Lambretta.
Sheas sinn air mullach na beinne
Bàta MacBrayne a' tighinn
Ice cream gach Diciadain.

Ladhairean crùbaig air starsaich Granny
An togsaid, an abhainn, an cladach
Crìochan sona na laithean saora.

Sgothan beaga nan crogainn
'gam putadh a mach
Ballaisd, raoid,
Dathan brèagha
Doimhneachd dorch
Suez Crisis Looms

Tràighean m'òigrigh
Na rùin èibhinn
Is trioblaidean an t-saoghail
Mar dhuilleag sealasdair a thogadh air cuidhil

*(*Bha an laoidh – sa air a sheinn air an latha mu
dheireadh den 'term')*

TAKE AND BLESS OUR HOLIDAYS – O CAUSA NOSTRA LAETITIAE

The last day of school
The final hymn of the term
Maquisards of the glen
Playing at Cosa Nostra
The world of Al Capone –
Don't tell, or you're dead!!

We rendezvous at the poles
For Hide and Seek and
Make up kitchen dressers
New wars by the day
The Bay of Pigs, or
Who's the best?
The Barrachs or the Uibhisteachs?

I ran with my circle
Clink and clank down the hill
As fast as a Lambretta
We stood on the top of the hill
MacBrayne's Steamer in sight
Ice cream on Wednesdays.

Crab claws on Granny's doorstep
The water trough,
The river, the seashore
Delightful margins of our freedon days.

Little tin boats
Shoved out
Ballast, mooring
Bright colours
Dark depths
Suez Crisis Looms

The strands of my childhood
As joyful mysteries
The world and its cares,
Lifted like the iris leaf into the whirl.

MOIRE MHATHAIR 'S A PÀISDE FON TURAID FAIRE

Moire Mhathair 's a pàisde
Fon Turaid Faire
Chan eil agad ach aon diòn
Do chul ri solais nach dìbir
'S iad gu buan a' creachadh
Ar neo–chiontais.
An latha ciùin
A'cromadh air falbh
Bho bhealach Ruaidheabhal
Gu muir farsainn.
Tha ghrian a'tuiteam mar dhortadh-fala
Meuran dearg ag achanaich
Tro sgurran an dorachadais.
Ach tusa nad dhiobhaireachd
Caol, ciatach, mar iteag
Nad ìomhaidh do ghinealach ùr
Comhdaichte nad chleòca fionn-gheal
Fiamh a'ghàire air do ghnuis
'S tu làn dòchais mar mhàthair
Do phàisde air a thogail suas
Cinnteach gun toir E buaidh
Fada thairis air Ground Zero 's Guantanamo
Ged thèid laithean ar n-aithreachais nan smàl.

MADONNA AND CHILD OF THE
ROCKET RANGE

Madonna and Child
Below the Watch Tower
Your one defence
A cold shoulder turned on perpetual lights
Tracking down our innocence
In the gentle falling of day
From Rueval hill
To the wide sea
The sun rolls as red as any blood
Crimson fingers supplicating
Before cliffs of darkness.
And you, impenetrable, pencil slim
An icon for a new age
In creamy understated folds
Your hesitant smile
Hopeful as any mother,
You hold your child aloft
Knowing he will make his mark
Far beyond Ground Zero and Guantanamo
To the end of all of our remorseful days
Though all our yesterdays are pulverised to earth.

David Neilson

STRATHCLYDE BANQUETS

From *Robert the Vole*

Hedebangr stood at the handiest door for the top table, straining to see from a high window how low the sun was. 'Where is it he's fae?' he said.

'Naples,' said Number One.

'He's in place?'

Number One nodded, and Hedebangr signalled. The horns blared a raucous shout leaping to the rafters, where smoke hung twisting, dipping through the gap in the roof. The dishes were conveyed on long trestles ranged over the flagstones. Above them waved the pennants of St Senga, emblazoned with green and gold.

Hedebangr moved swiftly to the top table and slid into his seat, waving away his attendants.

'Imminence,' he said, smiling at the stranger, robed in red, who stood up at his approach.

'Majesty,' said Gennaro, bowing.

'Ye fur soup?' said Hedebangr, indicating plenty. Gennaro surveyed the fare, his impressive nose jutting from a face underset with a dark fleshy chin and puffy jowls. A boy laid an iron dish, heaped with halved macaroon bars, at the top table.

'It's Italian soup,' said Hedebangr. 'Tar somethin.'

Gennaro's nostrils flared, and his eyelids rose slightly.

Hedebangr snapped his fingers. 'Soup expert,' he said.

'*Tartarughe in brodo*,' said Number One.

'Ah,' said Gennaro. 'It is on behalf of your renowned aide here that your majesty has laid claim to a red hat.'

But Hedebangr was scowling at the Lord Shug, who was slipping into his seat. He inclined his head towards Number One. 'Jiss fill us in whenever.' He spread his hands out before them. 'Some place, eh?'

Behind them the orb of the world was depicted on a great weaving across the back wall. At its edge there was Beyond, then the Back of Beyond, and then Coatbridge. In the centre, colourfully painted, were the great buildings of Strathclyde, on all of which you could see three sides and most of the roof: the School, with its proud motto *Pilam et trochum et socium noli in viam sequi*; the Bishop's seat at St Senga's; and leading down from that to the cross with Under the Willows, Cathedral Street, while on an incline just to the north stood the elaborate fane of St Imbroglio, and at the bottom of a steep dip the head-quarters of the Strathclyde Development Guild. Slightly to the east of this was a large public square dominated at the far end by the vault of the Hedethebaw Memorial.

The tureens came forward, shoulder high, on wooden boards. Gennaro traced the uncials along a rim. 'Milanda?' he said.

'Naw, the baker's here,' said Hedebangr. 'Banquetware.'

•

They looked through the shattered arch, at the dark howe under the grey green sky. Before them rose a great mound of broken sandstone, blocks tumbled one atop the other, dropped and dragged to form a vague barrelled shape. From a gap a stunted elder pointed, having taken root in earthy crevices; across another rippled the sinewy haunch of a marble beast.

They scuffed over the rubble, stumbling on half bricks, terracotta rooftiles and cracked pipes. Bracken and fern were scrambling from a ditch that circled the heap, and a fingery wisp of smoke waved this way then that out of a hole in the roof, twisting at sedate clear angles, there blowing little wind.

Robert the Vole lifted ironshod feet, moving slowly towards a door four times his height. On the cracked pebbly doorstep the remains of a diamond pattern, in dark brown or black, could still be read. The timbers, studded with rusty nail-heads like crown pieces, were cross-sparred and painted a faded blue. A dark keyhole, twice as long as a man's hand, its iron escutcheon rotted and worn, had been bored just out of reach. Stepping back again, he could pick out the characters engraved in the brass plate screwed into the centre of the door: *J. McFALL.*

'Any port in a storm, eh?' said McDowall.

'Indeed,' said Robert the Vole, gazing ahead.

Behind them a crow fluttered, doing giant steps and baby steps.

Robert the Vole lifted a heavy branch and struck the door three times. McDowall came up behind him and peered up at the lock. 'Dono if ah fancy this,' he said.

Robert the Vole shrugged. 'Any port in a storm,' he said.

They heard a scraping behind the door. Something was dragged behind it, and the bolt fumbled with. After several clanks it was finally grasped and flung back. Then there was scraping again as something was dragged away.

The door opened very slowly. McDowall looked up and saw soft fingers like young treetrunks grasp the edge.

Robert the Vole saw a child eight feet high, bending over to look at them in the light of a torch burning overhead in the hall. It was naked save for an undershirt of woven hemp which frayed at its waist. Its blond hair, red in the torchlight, was matted, and its nose was running.

'Maaamy,' it said, suddenly. McDowall stood back, covering his ears.

'Whit?' said a sharp voice, like the grinding of an distant axle.

'Good evening,' called Robert the Vole. 'We are two weary travellers seeking shelter for the night.'

A dark bulk moved up behind the child. 'Whit hiv ah told you aboot that door?' she shouted, slapping the child on the side of the head and grasping it by the upper arm. It bawled, and as McDowall reeled, she pulled it away, struggling. Robert the Vole ducked as it tried to kick her.

'Whit ye wantin?' she said. Robert the Vole looked up at a face eight feet above him and a yard long.

'Mrs McFall?' said Robert the Vole. She had grey-blond hair, pulled back tight, a thin mouth, deep-pitted cheeks and sharp lines on her forehead between her eyebrows.

'Aye. Whit ye wantin?'

'Refuge from the coming storm,' he said. He looked at the bawling child, which was hanging on to her skirt and peering out from behind her leg.

'A delightful child,' he smiled. 'Does he go to playgroup?'

She looked at him, her eyes narrowing. McDowall smiled wanly.

'A dry corner in which to lay one's head, a little food...'

'Food,' she said, dragging the word out. She opened the door further. It creaked on rusty hinges and scraped over the flagging. 'Haud oan till ah tell him...'

•

Goblets of Tizer were poured before them. Hedebangr broke off a hunk of bread and dipped it in his cup.

'Get wired in,' he said. 'There neeps in aspic therr.'

Gennaro stood at his chair.

'*In nomine patris et filii et spiritus sancti*,' he said, blessing himself. Hedebangr copied him rapidly, as did the other diners.

'It's an authentic recipe,' he said, as Gennaro sat.

'Trophy of some southern excursion, *senz'altro*,' said the Cardinal. A page, at his left elbow, settled his ermine.

'Fair do's,' said Hedebangr, wiping Tizer from his brow and spreading his palms. 'Archduke Luigi shoutit fur handers.'

The page dodged over, kneeling before Hedebangr, who ladled in some of the broth from the steaming tureen. 'Thirz a big wan at the tap here,' he said, drawing his dagger. 'Lissen,' he said to the page, looking up unobtrusively and nodding down the benches, 'gauney go doon an tell him tae stoap lickin his plate?'

Plunging his hand in the tureen and jerking it upwards, he speared a tortoise and deposited it upside down in the Cardinal's broth, its paws breaking the surface as it floated.

'Howz it ye dae this again?' he said, looking at his own soup bowl.

Gennaro extracted the tortoise with thumb and forefinger, shook the broth off and cracked the shell against the rim of his bowl. He prised the edges apart and the tortoise slid out into the soup.

'Ah,' he said, nodding and inclining his glass in Hedebangr's direction, '*al dente.*'

Hedebangr rose to his feet and held up his goblet.

'*Al dente!*'

He drank a great draught of Tizer and dashed his goblet against the fireplace. Everyone else held up his drinking horn and cried, '*Al dente!*'

•

They stepped over the threshold into a certain odour. McDowall skirted round the child, whose head seemed to occupy most of its body, and who was still standing at the door. In the hallway, which was dark other than where the torch blazed, corrugated cardboard had been strewn. A panelled door lay ahead of them, past a massive coal bunker.

'Away through,' said Mrs McFall, slamming the door behind them and throwing the bolt.

Robert the Vole walked into a steamy kitchen seven yards high. Above him was a pulley thick with clothes, sheets and blankets. In the left wall was a tall window, over the lower half of which a net curtain had been strung. From the pelmet above long curtains of royal blue hung down. Outside, barely discernible in the gloom, monstrous nappies like sails were blowing on a line which was held out by a pole protruding from below the window ledge. Beside the window, a door into a scullery lay half-open.

In the middle of the kitchen was a table with lathed table-legs, brown varnished, the girth of columns. Over it was spread a faded white tablecloth, with cupstains the circumference of buckets, and open lacework in the centre.

Robert the Vole suddenly became aware, behind him and to his left, of a bed recess as big as a stable. Lying in a brass bed-stead, heaped over with a sandwich of patched bedclothes, was a man about five yards long, if those were his feet which were bundled at the near end. He was bristle-chinned, with thick black eyebrows, thinning on the top with wild hair frizzled at the sides. It was difficult to tell, since he lay unmoving, whether he was looking at them with his eyes half-closed, or whether he was sleeping.

'Ah wis gauney get this place tidied up,' said Mrs McFall, coming in behind them.

'You needn't trouble,' said Robert the Vole. 'It's charming.'

'Here, sit doon,' she said. 'Thae seats ur a bit big.' She pulled a wooden stool from underneath the kitchen table and slid it over to them. It was long enough for both, though McDowall's knees were close to his shoulders.

'That's great,' said McDowall. 'Ah like a hard seat.'

He jumped halfway up the seat as the tablecloth rustled to a long growl.

'He'll no touch ye,' said Mrs McFall, bending over and lift-ing the tablecloth on her side. 'Jist ye be good,' she said. 'Aye, ah like a hard seat an aw, bit he disnae.' She moved to the sink and turned on the tap to fill the kettle, which looked like a hip-bath. 'Ahm that stupit,' she said. 'Ah thoat that wis you roon wi thae communion tickets.' She turned to McFall. 'You hate thaim, don't ye?'

McFall grunted.

'He hates thaim,' she said. 'Ah aye say ye've tae live an let live.'

'That's whit ah say as well,' said McDowall, looking down.

'Ye take a cup a tea?' she said. 'Ahl make a wee piece. Ahm makin Jim tea anyhow. Naw, he hates them, bit tae ma mind they dae a lot a good. Thir aye willin tae help.'

'Whit ur ye here fur if ye canny help sumdi?' said McDowall.

'Ah know,' she said. 'That's ma warcry.'

She dipped into the breadbin on the sideboard and took out half a loaf.

The kettle was coming to the boil. She buttered one of the slices and spooned some tea into the teapot, pouring on the boiling water.

'Thae eggcups,' she said brightly. She opened the sideboard door and took out the eggcups with Humpty Dumpty shapes delineated in thick black lines. For herself, she took out a teacup that looked like an earthenware plantpot, and for McFall a mug like a wishing well.

She spread jam on the slices of bread and put some aside to cut up in four sections. They lay on the teaplate looking like marble floor tiles.

'Oh, ah forgot,' she said, going to the larder. 'There a snowball here as well.' She brought out a packet of snowmen's heads and deposited it on the table.

'Ah fancy wan a them,' said McDowall.

She poured some of the tea into an old oilcan, mixing it with the same amount of milk, and stirred it with a ladle before squeezing a top with a raised drinking slot back on to it.

'You like yir tea, don't ye?' she said to the child, who stood behind a chair, looking at Robert the Vole and McDowall between the slats. He had a dummy in his mouth. It was coloured in red and white, was stencilled with the word *Emergency*, and had the remains of a hawser hanging from it. He trailed his teddy by the arm: an extremely realistic bear, Robert the Vole thought, which was growing thin in patches and even had an ursine smell. Its eyes were closed.

●

Hedebangr gestured to a waiter, who brought up a board. 'Fancy a roll an tottie scone? Good touch that, intit? Servin them in paper pokes twistit at the end?'

'*No, grazie*,' said Gennaro. 'You must recall, to crown a new prince of the church is a step of the utmost significance.'

'Aye, tae us, ur the Taurry Rope?' said Hedebangr.

Gennaro frowned.

'I am sorry, this dialect...'

'Naw, sorry,' said Hedebangr. 'You're sayin that ye'd be lookin fur the fulfilment a numerous conditions, basically...' He gestured in the air, then spoke with a flourish. 'As performance indicators in the domain a sanctity.'

'Let me cite an example,' said Gennaro. 'It is arguably outrageous to forward initial application taxes in the form of pontifical plate and cutlery seized in brigandage.'

'We've never been in Brigandage,' said Shug.

'This is conussoor patter,' said Hedebangr, lifting his plate a foot from the table. 'Faur as ahm concerned it's a plate. Ahv never even looked at the boattum ae it.'

'This,' said Gennaro, indicating his dish, 'is white enamel with a blue edge. Scarcely the prey of brigands. And it does not have a triple tiara stamped in the edge.'

'Mine's git Army & Navy stores,' said Shug. 'They knives an spoons are good anaw. See how they aw fit thegither?'

'Okay,' said Hedebangr, sighing, 'obviously it wis the Pope's, bit Luigi says it wis discounted stock.'

Gennaro opened his mouth to speak, but Hedebangr was looking round and holding up his hand.

'Time furra song,' he said. He signalled, and the band struck up a drum roll. 'Whiddyiz fancy?'

'*Hedethebaw*!' someone shouted.

'Very good,' said Hedebangr. '*Hedethebaw* it is.'

The drum roll lessened a little, and the fiddles skirled quietly. Hedebangr cleared his throat, settled his stance, and began.

> *Hedethebaw lay in the park*
> *The cans were by his side*
> *He hid but rolled his jersey up*
> *When an eldritch sight he spied.*

> *A wizened guy was overheid*
> *Up near the Spion Kop.*
> *'Now, Hedethebaw, git aff yir mark*
> *For you will reach the top.'*

'All hail, prophetic wizened guy.'
He scrambles oan tae wan knee,
'Fur who can see the things tae come
But the prince of grammary?'

'Aw naw, aw naw, brave Hedethebaw,
That name is no fur me.
I'm but a fan uv the great Tarzan
An ah live in the eildon tree.

'The King's in Partick Burgh Halls
Drinkin the blood red wine.
He started at the crack a dawn,
He's been oot his skull since nine.

'Arise an get yir band a men
An take them aw in hand
An march them oot a fair Ruchhill
South-west tae Anniesland.'

Tae Anniesland they've took the road
By the auld gasometer bright
An there they've stood fur hauf an oor
Jist waitin fur the lights.

Sammy the Glaikit he's rose in wrath
He's tied his helmet oan
He's took his lucky pencil stump
An a primitive Vodaphone.

'I do not fear bold Hedethebaw
No matter whit the score
But I do fear the terminus
Of the number forty-four.'

Now Sammy's men are cut tae shreds
They never hid a chance
For his bold foemen jumped the lights
An come oot every junction at wance.

Oh the birk will blossom in the spring
And wither in the fall,
And never more will Sammy sit
In Partick Burgh Halls.

•

Mrs McFall lifted a sack of sugar and poured it into McFall's mug, which she took over to him as he eased himself up slowly from the pillow. He blew on his tea and took a long slurp. When he had finished, he took a horse's bite out of the bread and slumped again. He chewed and swallowed, looking round at Robert the Vole and McDowall. Robert the Vole found himself wondering why there was no light in McFall's eyes. Only after a moment did it occur to him to consider the size of the pupils.

Mrs McFall handed the teacups to Robert the Vole and McDowall, along with the sandwiches.

'So whit brings ye oot here, then?' she said. 'We don't see mini folk on this road here.'

'Family business,' said McDowall. 'Stuff ah hid tae attend tae.'

'And did ye get it attended tae?'

'Oh aye. Nae bother. But we goat loast.'

'Who wis it?' she said. 'Dae ah know them?'

'Dono,' said McDowall. 'Dye know the McNeills?'

'Maimie McNeill?'

'Aye. Dye know her?'

'Auch, ah know her nur man. They're a good distance, urnt they?'

'Aye,' said McDowall. 'Well, ah dono.'

'Ah know her,' she said. 'Imagine gettin loast oot here.'

A millstone suddenly ground to life.

'Sippose ah better git up.'

McFall laid the mug just underneath the bed.

With a sigh, followed by a loud exhalation of breath, he rolled away the bedclothes. He lay for a moment, scratching his chest. Then he stretched. He pulled away the bedclothes with his knees and swung his legs out of bed. He was wearing white shorts as well as his undershirt.

He looked down at Robert the Vole from the edge of the bed, his eyes heavy and his mouth unmoving. He closed his eyes and yawned.

'Well, that's me up.'

The side of his hand flashed up and knocked Robert the Vole across the kitchen table, where, pulling down the cake-stand, he lay.

There was a loud barking from under the table. McDowall looked at the ogre, his eyes wide, uttering no sound.

'Auch, Jim,' said Mrs McFall. 'Thiv no hid thir snowball.'

•

Gennaro sat, unshaven, in a long white shirt, his eyelids heavy, his fingers cupping an empty plain white bowl. A badger mantle was slumped over his wide shoulders, spilling on to the floor about his feet. There was a sudden bang behind the serving hatches. A tremor passed through him, followed by another, crashing about him like a wave before the first had stopped resounding. Somebody was shouting wildly. The words would be hard to make out anyway, but Gennaro felt more than unusually cut off from the uncouthness of English. He could tell, though, that the message was insistent, and the words, despite his reluctance, started to fall into place. Was that *ashet*? Ashet pie? He thought he knew the names of most of the animals. But there were odd things in the forest here, and some... well, not officially animals, at least not after the age of seven.

That was more like something being thrown, Gennaro imagined, wincing, like a large brazen serving tray careening off a wall, hard enough to strike sparks.

'Two thousand ashet pies!' The voice was clear enough now. How could anyone be that hoarse and loud at the same time? '*Two thousand*?'

There seemed to be some sort of murmur. The silences didn't last long enough to tell. Why was he caring? He closed his eyes and ran two fingers lightly down the cleft in his forehead. The murmur was there, certainly: half defensive from its tone, half petulant.

'Two thousand?' The roar was nearer. Gennaro was con-scious of a tall figure in the doorway behind the serving hatch. 'Naw, naw, you canny write that noo.' A finger was being jabbed in the air, aimed at someone. 'That's a factor a ten.'

Hedebangr turned into the main hall, scowling. 'Two thousand ashet pies,' he growled. He came and stood at the end of the table. He unbuckled his sword, legs wide, and threw the scabbard down on the table.

A tremor passed through Gennaro. He closed his eyes and shook slightly, and then opened them again.

'Morning,' said Hedebangr, looking about him. 'Great day, eh?'

'Uh,' said Gennaro, looking down.

'Whit ye fur?'

The kitchen was a long room lined by bounding arches. Through one gap, in the centre, was a counter where someone in an apron was rubbing a white china mug, which he was holding upside down, with a cloth. On the back wall was the Shettleston Tapestry, with the Milngavie Giant, a freak of nature who, though but sixteen, had grown to five feet eleven and could hurl a ginger bottle one hundred yards; and many of these, during the sultry April of 893, he had rained upon the school dinner wagons that he pirated for extra custard, laying waste the caravan and refusing to show his dinner ticket. In a lonely defile near Carbeth he had gone to ground, pursued by armed inspectors, homecraft advisors and a posse of cafe owners. He had, at the last, spurned the offer of an Imperial amnesty and an introduction to management course, and was now depicted lying at full length, Hedebangr's foot planted on his chest, below neatly stitched Carolingian characters reading *That's me tae buy a new hatchet.*

Gennaro looked up, his brows knitted. His greyish hair was flying off at the side and his cheeks were sunken underneath the bone.

Hedebangr nodded at the bowl.

'A cappuccino.' Gennaro spoke from the depths of his throat.

'Sounds good,' said Hedebangr. 'Two cups a cino, then.'

He looked round for a moment, paused, and then strode over to the counter.

Gennaro was conscious, out of the corner of his eye, of Hedebangr gazing up at some ikons above the counter, show-ing stylised beakers and dishes of some sort.

'Naw, lissen,' he heard Hedebangr saying, 'jist gies a Mug O' Tea.'

Gennaro looked closely at a crack in the table that ran across his line of vision, splitting into branches and offshoots around the knots and whorls of the wood.

Then Hedebangr was back, swinging his legs round under the table and sitting down on the bench which ran along the length of the table on the other side from Gennaro, whose eyes were fixed on the parcel of greaseproof paper, dotted with tiny red and blue stars, that Hedebangr put down in front of him.

Hedebangr opened his own packet, unwrapping half of it, and took a large bite. He nodded sideways, chewing.

Someone came up beside Gennaro and put down a glass cup full of a fawn liquid, topped with a thin froth, on a glass saucer. He set a steaming mug beside Hedebangr, turning the handle towards him.

Gennaro, sitting with his forehead against the fist of his left hand, flicked up the nearest flap of his packet with his right forefinger and prised the paper further wide. It was something dark, extremely rough textured, in a bread roll that was brown on top and white underneath.

Gennaro gazed at the roll and eased it halfway out of its packet. He lifted the top and saw a rectangle of fried meat.

'Squerr sausage,' said Hedebangr. 'Never see it anywherr else.'

Gennaro closed the top of the roll again and relaid the paper around it with a finger. He sighed, and his left hand fished somewhere in a low pocket. It came up with a string of beads, which he fingered, staring ahead.

'Good night last night, eh?' said Hedebangr.

Kathleen O'Rourke

MARMITE

One Monday evening, I was sitting on the verandah drinking gin (my Lenten penance), and watching Mount Bwabwa, that great disordered bing, sink into the filmy distance. All I could hear was the sounds of children being called in ('Nah-oh-me!' from Mrs Chavula next door), and the apologetic homeward putterings of volunteers' motorbikes (only 250 cc's, only ones in town.) The occasional passer-by nodded over. 'Matandara,' I called back. I wasn't drinking alone if people could see me, was I?

Suddenly, I had one of those urgent needs you get that you can't immediately identify. Sex, a drink, a ciggie, a cup of tea? Home, even when you are home? And then I knew exactly what I wanted – a taste of goat.

Well. It's Marmite that expats are supposed to yearn for, though I've never really understood why. Perhaps its nursery taste kept the old nanny colos mindful of the order and rituals they were trying to uphold. But why would anyone else be wearying for the stuff? As far as I recall, it's got a strong gamey taste, sort of primitive and exotic: you'd still crave that in Africa? But maybe it was the motherly jar expats loved, so strong and sturdy, its lid so secure... The gin was beginning to numb me nicely – but I still wanted some goat.

Next day in the staff room, I interrupted the lunch time chat.

'Eh, sorry, everybody. I have a problem. Maybe someone can help me. It's this: how can I get a goat?'

'A goat? Why are you wanting a goat, Jane?' asked Mrs Longwe.

'For a party. An Easter party. For everybody.'

It was like announcing a stay-back in a Bargeddie pub.

Then Mr Chavula's voice broke through. 'Mr Moyo is the man you should consult, Miss Brown. He has a cousin in Livestock.'

Mr Moyo was our new school secretary. His office smelled of ripe bananas and Gestetner skins. He was thin and nervous and his white cuffs were fraying.

'A goat, madam? For a party? I have heard of your wonderful parties.'

'Thank you, Mr Moyo. Perhaps you would like to come?'

'Of course! But unfortunately some of my cousins from Barandi will be staying at my house at that time.'

'They too are invited, Mr Moyo. There'll be plenty of food.'

In the staff room the discussion was still going on.

'Was Mr Moyo able to help you?'

'No problem!' Everybody smiled at me and at each other.

'But now – what should I pay for a goat?'

'I think,' said Jacob Chavula, 'you must proceed with great caution, Miss Brown.' Mr Chavula was our Science teacher. He had an Honours degree in Physics, he lived next door to me, and he spent every weekend singing American evangelical hymns, solo or in quartet. He had also borrowed every portable substance in my house.

'Bargaining can be a most delicate process,' he continued. 'This is to be expected, of course, particularly when it involves those who are not yet fully conversant with the culture and customs of the other party.'

'What would you pay for a goat, Mr Chavula?' I asked.

'For myself, I have never been so fortunate as to consider buying one; but Mrs Longwe here says her cousin, the one who works for the Government, paid twenty kwacha for a goat for his daughter's wedding.'

Next day wee Mr Moyo said twenty kwacha was fine. I paid him a deposit of ten kwacha, and he promised to do his levelbest to get the goat to me early on Good Friday morning.

• • •

On Maundy Thursday the students left for home. By lunch time Friday my house was speckless. Esther, my home help, her mother, the gardener, and two of the casual workers had done a grand job. (Before I came to Africa, I was of course not going to have servants; but I could not resist the desperation of those who came to my door begging for any kind of work. And – how nice it was to have the wood cut, the fire lit, the ironing done; and all their wages cost me, in total, was ten kwacha a week. I know, I know: but I could not pay much more than the going rate. What would THAT have started?)

The party was to be in the garden, and Mr Chavula had strung up some lights among the frangipani and bougainvillea. The effect was gorgeous. My only concern was that we might

be polluted with flying ants, as we'd been some days before.
These creatures had really spooked me, when they'd erupted
out of the earth with their link-sausage bodies and Rizla wings,
had whirred up and down for a couple of minutes, and then
died twitching on the floor. It wouldn't really matter, anyway,
if they did come: I'd once seen a student pluck some of them
out of the air and crunch them like a couple of Pringles.

5 o'clock came, and still no goat. Mr Moyo had assured me
before he'd left for the bank on Friday morning that the goat
would have arrived by 2 o'clock in the afternoon. He'd looked
weary. He'd been deaved all week, as I'd been, with enquiries
about the goat. There had been long staff discussions about it.
I'd been told the outcomes: Mr Chavula and Mr Sibale would
supervise the killing; Chavula would organise the cooking.
Chavula and Sibale would share the most coveted part of the
goat, the intestines. They'd offered them to me, but I'd declined.

At 6 o'clock an agitated Chavula told me he'd been to Mr
Moyo's house to find that Mr Moyo had gone to his sister in
Elani. 'But do not worry, Jane,' said Mr Chavula. 'I shall visit
Mr Moyo's brother in Livestock tomorrow morning. You can
accompany me in your car.'

That night it rained for hours, vicious, terrifying, tropical
rain, but it had been off for a good while when Mr Chavula and
I set out for the market about eight o'clock. We had just stopped
at the school gate when another car drove up, and out came
Sheila Anderson. Sheila and her husband Alistair had been in
Chipasa for only two months. They were Scots, Civil Servants
who'd taken early retirement to help out in the Mission
Hospital down the road, and we still had that intense initial
closeness that springs up between compatriots abroad.

'Good morning, dear,' said Sheila. 'I thought I'd come early
and help you. I had to take Alistair down to the garden to plant
his maize. And I've brought some beer for the party.'

'Oh great, Sheila,' I said. 'I'm glad you're here. I've got to
go and see about the bloody goat. It hasn't arrived. Mr Chavula
and I are going to see Mr Moyo's brother in the market. Can
you come with us?'

'Oh poor Jane! Never a dull moment with you, dear. Of
course I'll come. Look, I'll put the beer in your boot, and we
can leave our car with Alistair on the way down.'

At the market, we clumped along the shaky duckboards in
our Wellingtons, past the stalls selling old clothes, ufa flour out

of scoured oil cans, single batteries, chickens in baskets, loose cigarettes (non-export rejects: they smoked like used cat litter), and piles and piles of bananas and mangoes. We finally reached the livestock area, a small makeshift pen in a far corner. Two men wearing tattered Wimpey oilskins, and a boy, all with bare feet, were standing round a wee smoky fire. Three bedraggled calves were tied to the pen.

Mr Chavula addressed the men. (Mr Chavula's English had created a new verb in our circle – to chavule. It means when someone speaks a second language so perfectly that when you're listening to it, you don't hear what's being said because you're lost in admiration at the impeccable syntax and exact vocabulary. Dutch politicians are great chavulers, by the way.)

Anyway, Mr Chavula clearly chavuled in all tongues, for it was fifteen minutes before he and the boy came over to Sheila and me.

'Your animal, Miss Brown, is, I regret, not here.'

'What?' I said. 'Where is it then? Which is Mr Moyo's brother? What's happened?'

'Mr Moyo's brother is absent. He too has gone to his sister, whose child is ill. It does not behove us to enquire any further.'

'I am sorry, Mr Chavula. Please convey my sympathy. But what about the goat? Where is it exactly?'

'It is at the home of Mr Moyo's grandmother.'

'Why does she have it? Where does she live?'

'She resides at the edge of the escarpment, on the road to Dedza. This young man here, whose name is Mr Lungu, has offered to guide us to her home. You and Madam Anderson can take us there in your car. It will be a simple expedition.'

• • •

For the first couple of miles, up to the small stadium where the Life President had held a rally some years before, the Dedza road was tarmac. From there on it was a potholed track, deeply rutted with those peculiar horizontal furrows that no one, not even a snooty UN engineer, had been able to explain to me; and it was very very slippy. I drove up it slowly and carefully, wishing it was as gritted as my teeth. None of us spoke. Then we rounded a bend, and I saw that the next bit was a deep and viscous bog.

'Sorry,' I said. 'That's it. We can't go through there.'

'Now what?' said Sheila. 'Will we just have to go back home?'

'Well, I can't see what else to do,' I replied.

'Never mind, dear,' she said. 'Nobody can say you didn't do your best.'

'No, no, all is not over,' said Mr Chavula from the back. 'Mr Lungu and I will go to the grandmother's house. You ladies can wait here, and we shall bring back the sheep that is lost.' At that, he and the boy jumped out of the car and disappeared through the dense scraggy bushes at the side of the track.

Sheila and I looked around. The vast African sky was thick and grey and shiny like steel wool. Atmosphere and visibility were dull and depressed. Normally there were wonderful views from this road: in fact to the east you could see as far as the Livingstone Mountains in Tanzania. Yes, he'd been here, the great doctor, in his obsessive drive further and further into Africa – or further and further away from lowering old Lanarkshire? I'd been reared about six stony miles away from Blantyre, his own native village, and so I knew exactly where he was coming from, the good grim crazy sod. Today, however, we could see only the heavy sky, the charcoal branches of the bushes sketched on the graphite-grey horizon, and the greasy orange road. I headed off the imponderables that Sheila loved.

'Right, Sheila, I spy with my little eye something beginning with O...R.'

'Oh? Oh, well, all right. Is it inside or outside the car?'

'Outside.'

'Old road? Oily road? Orange road?'

We made up really hard ones: flaking blue eyeshadow; invisible coffee plantation; silly women playing daft games.

Twenty minutes was enough.

'Sheila, tell me about your father. What kind of man was he?'

'What do you mean, Jane?'

'Well, say I went through the alphabet. Was he ambitious? brutal? carnaptious? devious?'

'Oh no, no, no. He was a very good-living man.' Sheila went on to tell me how he'd been an Insurance man; he'd supported Stenhousemuir; he liked things quiet and orderly; and I began to see why she'd married her pernickety Alistair – and also why she'd come to Africa. God forgive me as a nosey besom; but people do love to talk.

Then we discussed our most embarrassing moments; our first kiss; celebrities we couldn't stand. This took us up to half twelve; and then I had one of Sheila's beers. Her face curdled slightly, but I said my neuritis was bad. Then we sang songs we'd learned from school radio programmes; then I had another beer.

Around half-past two a pick-up came from Dedza way, and Mr Chavula and the boy Lungu stepped down from the cab.

'Hi, ladies! Good news! I have found the animal, and this gentleman, who is taking wood to Chipasa, gave us a lift.'

Mr Chavula let down the tailgate of the lorry, and out climbed an elderly man wearing an Ireland rugby shirt. He pulled behind him a very dirty and unkempt little goat, which bleated weakly as it found its feet on the skittery surface.

'This is the owner of the animal,' said Mr Chavula, 'although it was with Mr Moyo's grandmother.'

The tiny goat turned and stood in silence. It fixed its eldritch eyes on me. I felt odd, and very uncomfortable.

'This man is not yet paid,' said Mr Chavula. 'He and the old woman live in direst poverty.'

'OK, Mr Chavula. Here's five kwacha, and he can get the rest from Mr Moyo.' I realised I would never know the full story of the goat's provenance.

'And the driver, Jane?' said Chavula.

By this time the driver had got out of the cab, and was looking at me too. The goat whimpered again, more painfully, and stamped its small wedge heels into the glutinous mud.

'Yes, of course, Jacob,' I said. 'Can you ask him to take the goat to my house?'

Chavula, Lungu and the 'owner' chatted amicably for five minutes. The rest of us – Sheila, the goat, and me – were nearing the end of our tethers.

'Yes, Miss Brown,' said Chavula. 'The driver will deliver the sheep for five kwacha.'

'The goat, you mean. Fine. Great. Here you are.'

'And Jane, Mr Lungu says he too is worthy of his hire. Without him we would have nothing.'

'What! That's not my fault! He can see Mr Moyo as well.'

But I looked down at the boy's bony purple feet, all spattered with orange muck, and I gave him five kwacha too.

'Now – let's go.'

'I,' said Chavula, 'shall of course go with the sheep.'

'Goat, Mr Chavula,' said Sheila. 'It's a goat.'

'It's a Maravi sheep,' said Mr Chavula.

It took us forty minutes to get back on the tar. When we reached her house, Sheila said in her People's Friend voice, 'Well, dear, that WAS an interesting afternoon! What a story it will make for my newsletter to the folks back home. Thank you! See you at four tomorrow.'

Later that evening, I looked over into Chavula's garden. I could hear a faint plangent sound from behind his henhouse. Chavula came out and said, 'Matandara, Jane. Mr Sibale and I have decided to do the killing at daybreak. We shall first drain the blood and then extract the vital organs. Do you have any large cooking pots?'

'Pots? Yes, I have two.'

'That gives us ten – that should suffice. Two of them are really cauldrons.'

'Cauldrons? For the goat? Aren't you going to put it on a spit? Over the fire?'

I felt inordinately disappointed, I'm not sure why. Because there would be no sort of sacrifice, to make the little goat's death not so unnecessary? Because I wanted flames and smoke? Or was it just that stew was so – banal?

'No,' said Mr Chavula. 'A spit is primitive.'

And that was that. 'Primitive' is the ultimate argument clincher in Maravi.

That night I took two Valium in case I heard the goat die.

In the morning, over the fence, Mr Chavula said, 'It is dead. It made no sound. It was pregnant, too. Such animals are very humble, even in the Bible.'

'Yes,' I replied. 'Yes, Mr Chavula.'

And the party? Well, the staff and Esther and their relations and friends all arrived at four o'clock on the dot; and by the time the others joined the goat queue, there was none left. I didn't get any either – but by that time I'd completely lost the notion.

Walter Perrie

GIFTS

A lion she offered me, porcelain
couchant, four hands long, white underglaze
over-painted earth-russet and quizzical
as one of those mythical beasts of Hokusai
sly god-beasts asking; what do you hope for?

Also, later, a delicate man-wide bowl
austere and shallow, an ice-clear porcelain
horizon-rim scrolled in illegible
motifs of June-sky-blue and May-beech-green.

Ask what you wish for:
to have the lion guard my home;
to fill the bowl with honey.

Andrew Philip

NECTARINES

The fragrance of nectarines fills the hostel room.
It flowers through the few square metres, blossoms
around the coffee table, the open rucksacks,
the clothes draped haphazard over the two chairs.
It fuses with the summer evening sunlight, patiently
glowing its way through the tight-drawn, flimsy curtains,
and seems to swell the space into a grove.

The scent enters the two of them like a slow stimulant.
They breathe it off their hands like traces of spice,
like the linger of last night's garlic but sweet.
They feel it seep right through them, can inhale it now
through each other's skin from head to foot, hair to toe.
They have become fruit to each other, have become
windfall and harvest; fragrance, tang and zest.

Lydia Robb

SUBTOPIA

She's coming to cut my boots from my feet;
tells me my toenails are like Geisha-girls',
my plates, fossils in a curd of sweat.
Even now I listen for her shoes:
she says she always puts the left one on
before the right! This woman brings me
unwelcome gifts but will not drink or eat
under my roof. Elusive as sex,
she recoils from the currant-shaped shit
the rabbit lays on the hemstitched rug,
screws up her nose at the milk bottles.
Perfect urinals I've found. And what
about the sycamore growing through
the blistered kitchen floor?
Any moment now the door will admit her.
She'll conjure up illusions of space,
whitewashed rooms in a caring system;
with chilling words, put me in my place.

Hugh Clark Small

MIRROR LIFE, MIRROR DEATH

I'm a mirror lacking in ornate detail; a simple square wooden frame is all I offer those seeking embellishment around the face. My glass is dusty, my angle askew. I'm a mirror designated for the straightening of the tie or the quick consideration of stubble. Hanging here on an end wall, I see, on one extreme, a curtained window, on the other, a closed door. I can't see the room for the face of X. I'll tell you about the face...

The face is still wet from a jerky dousing of water (there is a sink directly beneath me). What strikes me first is the sheer ferocity of his stare. Two white beacons crowned with dark, bushy eyebrows. Eyes which do not merely reflect on the glass, but which rip through the wall, straight down the street and on, on, on towards some terrible horizon. The mirror as window; all-seeing, non-reflecting square.

Q – Why does X not just use the window?

A – The window only reflects grey buildings.

His haggard mouth moves without sound. Could be chewing a lozenge. Or a hideous thought.

'Come back to bed, X.'

A female voice calls out from behind the face, but his mouth keeps chewing in silence. The eyes stare rigid, malevolently into my glassy void. For ears so painfully protruding, you'd have thought...

'X, come back to the warm,' she attempts again, this time softer, pleading almost.

'I have to go.' The haggard mouth denies her with neither smile nor charm. A querulous look follows.

And sure enough, X leaves the confines of glass and wood. His head flashes round; a momentary blur of profile then hair. Standing facing her, I can tell you a secret about X which even he is unaware of. He is going bald! No one has pointed this out to him yet, not even she. His short brown hair is neatly cut, but it's that thinning, fleshy summit at the crown which gives him away. As if prompted by my observation, he runs his hand over his head to the nape of his neck, then walks directly away from me towards the girl.

'Look, I've got to go to work to earn money to pay for this god-forsaken place,' he gestures with crucified arms. 'I wish I didn't, but I do. That's the way it is, Porcupine.'

In calling the girl by her pet name, X releases himself from his foul mood. She kisses him swiftly on the lips as he bends towards her (an out-of-focus movement in the dusty glass), then she tumbles back onto the pillows.

'I'll see you around six,' he bids as he leaves the room.

She pulls the quilt over her head to drown out the thumping, resonating silence. A little whimper escapes every so often. Not asleep, just thinking under the feathers about this, that and the other. Furthermore, considering how to spend a whole weekday with X gone and no real plans to pursue. Well, except one...

However, since she will not rise again for at least two hours, I'll tell you something about the room I've been inhabiting since time immemorial.

The room is a fly-by-night shit hole. A couch-bed, two matching armchairs, a wardrobe, a tallboy, a sink, a curtained window, and me, the ever watchful mirror. That's all there is in this boarding house hideaway. Not even a token gesture to decoration in the form of picture or cheap ornament has been made. These things are either too ugly or they've been nicked by the last lodgers. So you see, their absence is well-founded.

And this current couple? Oh, they've been here about a fortnight or so. Some divorcee and his fancy bit. They talk big some nights about The Future, which keeps them sane. But then, The Future keeps everyone sane. It glows far away (always out of arm's reach); a transparent, pearly bubble filled full of life's every desire. Even now, she is half-asleep, half-dreaming of the bubble: a place of their own, X around all the time, maybe a couple of children.

'Dream on, Porcupine.'

I reflect over the stagnation of their predicament.

'Buzz, buzz, buzz, buzz, buzz...'

A fly lands on me, looking for a way out (everyone is). It parades round my square, feeling for escape with its grotesque black legs; giant tentacles at such close proximity. Its hideous eyes interrogate. I shudder to think of the germs it discards; no wonder my sheen is so tarnished. And no one ever thinks to clean me either.

'Buzz, buzz, buzz, buzz, buzz...'

The repetitive insect drilling noise; amplified and infuriating. Sleekit creature. Its pinprick brain gives up hope and it flies towards the curtains.

Meanwhile, the girl stirs and sobs again. She's still afraid to emerge from under the quilt to be greeted by a reality so bleak it bursts all her bubbles and instils depression.

But, after a while, reality must always be breached. The quilt ruffles and the girl spills out naked and forlorn. As she hurries towards me, the full-frontal scene starts to diminish; a gradual slicing off of knees, of hips, of waist, of breasts, so that, all I have in my sight, again, is a face. A beautiful, sad face this time. A face that's been hoping for too much and crying for too little. Rivulets of tears still show on her pink cheeks. Why does X call her Porcupine? I cannot guess.

Now she brushes her teeth. Foaming white mouth. Spit and slaver. Rinsing and smiling. Like X, she stares right through me. Eyes devour teeth, but her mind's eye probes much further. In this respect, I'm glad. My function becomes twofold:

(1) To reflect, and (2) To project.

I'm a glutton for self-endowed kudos.

She exits to a small bathroom on my right. I've never been hung in there, so I can't give you the run down. The toilet flushes, the shower pours, the drain gurgles. Quarter of an hour later, she's back in my domain. Swathed in a pink towelling dressing gown, she folds up the quilt, then pushes the bed back into the couch position. On this, she sits and fingers for her cigarettes. She lights up and exhales. Blue smoke unravels slowly. She's in no hurry to finish. Her eyes measure the boundaries of her cage; up, along, down, across. They even fall on me for a moment; a strange angle which reflects nothing but the cracked ceiling and the horrible lampshade.

Porcupine, I wonder... How do people get such strange names?

Mr Sumatra occupied the room about two years ago. He was a middle-aged, squat little man who lived out of his suitcase and drank gin straight from the bottle. Actually, he had two suitcases. In one, his clothes; in the other, samples of the wares he sold from door to door: time-saving kitchen gadgetry mostly, along with some dapper lines in silk bow-ties. He was an odd one was Mr Sumatra. Very odd.

Firstly, it was the girlie magazines. I mean, with the sink directly beneath me and all, I just didn't know where to look. Sometimes his rubbery, simian face would catch sight of its own sordid pleasure. He'd squirm, avert his guilt-ridden eyes, until, at last, at the climax, he'd focus again on the chosen glossy page. Doused in increasingly larger dosages of gin, he'd repeat the scenario every hour or so. Around midnight, all spirit and passion spent, he'd slink off to bed with a look of aberration and fall fast asleep.

This went on for a week or so without deviation to means or method. Then one night he returned home with a woman of similar age and attraction to his own. This made me think he hadn't bought her; she wasn't professional about it at all. They looked awkward together as they mixed their gins with small talk and tentative silences.

'Yes,' Mr Sumatra would say, 'the electric can-opener is one of my best sellers.'

He'd force the inanimate object into her hand. She'd fondle it for a few seconds then pass it back, looking a mite confused and slightly piqued.

'Maybe I'd better be going.'

'No, no, please stay. Here, have another gin.'

'It's awfully strong. Could you put something in it?'

'I'm afraid I've no tonic left,' he'd lie. 'Would some water do?'

And sure enough, he walked straight towards me, glass in hand, and turned the cold tap on. His face was bursting out in hot flushes of sweaty anticipation. Then he did it! He looked straight at me, at himself in reverse, and smiled in a manner which was at once frightening and obscene. His teeth, green and rickety, suggested a shark (in need of dentistry) about to slice through the plastic skin of some overblown inflatable floating loose on the ocean. Another couple of gins did the trick. Mr Sumatra, bless him for his sense of decorum, turned off all the lights.

This new interactive habit lasted for three more nights. On the fourth morning, he packed up both suitcases and left for good. His face still haunts me.

I'm not an attractive mirror. I admit it. Nice looking girls like Porcupine don't use me to make their faces up. They have dinky little vanity cases with mirrors of their own, usually concealed under the lid. Blue smoke still curling upwards, she goes through the rigmarole of foundation, eyeliner, rouge and lipstick. Beautification mirrors have it made. They never get guys like Mr Sumatra leering into them. They never have to undergo the degrading ritual of foaming white mouths, spits and worse... much worse! Where did I go wrong?

Porcupine looks great with all that stuff on. The sort of girl Mr Sumatra could only dream (or worse) about. Funny that I'm the link to both of them. Both their images concealed forever somewhere within my glassy particles. Molecules of ugliness and beauty colliding, repelling, refracting. Slowly but surely wearing me away; causing hairline cracks to form within my complex make up. And me, on the face of it, so solid yet fragile. An anomaly indeed.

Porcupine puts away her vanity case and extinguishes her cigarette in an ashtray. Coat on, she surveys the spartan surroundings, then turns on a heel and leaves the room. The blue smoke settles like morning mist on the sterile landscape of the furniture.

She's opened the curtains. Good. Some noon light to play with if I'm lucky. The grey buildings absorb most of it. They bounce it around, water it down, throw only the dull remnants my way. I don't complain. I mean, I don't really go in for that brash, fluorescent, chrome-plated lark. You know, every blemish and blackhead screaming to the fore. Who needs all that incriminating detail? Only the young and beautiful are brave enough for such meticulous scrutinisation. When the dust settles, they'll opt for something more becoming, something easier on the eye. Don't get me wrong, I'm no flatterer. I know I'm cheap and tawdry. But I'm no interrogator either and that's always a plus.

A lonely hour passes with only the damn fly for company.

'Buzz, buzz, buzz, buzz, buzz...'

Suddenly, a violence erupts. The door swings open, a loud thud at the end of it. The tallboy takes the brunt. Porcupine and X pour into the room ablaze with anger. She lights up, keeps her coat on. His eyes are spinning with disbelief.

'I can't believe you did that,' shouts X. 'You're so paranoid over nothing.'

'About you seeing your ex-wife on secret lunch dates, you mean.'

'We had some stuff to settle, that's all.'

'Over a bottle of wine and a meal. While I'm stuck in this shit-pit like some fucking concubine.'

'Look, Concu... Porcupine, calm down.'

'Calm fucking down! Look, this deal stinks, X. It doesn't work either way.'

'But if we give it time it...'

'Time! Time won't change these fucking curtains.'

She reaches over and gives the curtains an almighty yank. The plastic rail snaps and collapses at one end.

'Now look what you've done. Calm it will you. Here, sit down and we'll talk...'

'Don't fucking patronise me,' she screams as she kicks the armchair he's beckoned her towards.

'That's right, take it out on the furniture. Go on, Porcupine, let's see those spines jab.'

Ah! Porcupine. There's always a reason.

'Y-o-u f-u-c-k-i-n-g b-a-s-t-a-r-d.'

A slow insult often contains more volcanic venom than a quick volley of abuse. So it is with Porcupine. Her temper frayed, her reasoning AWOL, she rips me violently off the wall, grips my wooden frame with pincer-like precision. All these crazy new angles pour into me. I hear X shout 'No', I feel Mr Sumatra's ghost-smile tip and crackle through the length and breadth of my dust-disturbed surface. Then, with one foul swoop, I am flying, spinning, crashing hard against the wall I've faced since my inauguration. I ricochet down and land obliquely behind the couch bed. No blood, but I feel the death of a thousand fissures opening and exploding; shards of glass, multiplying and piercing.

With one final effort, I will Porcupine her lot; seven years' bad luck. Then everything goes black.

Julie Smith

THE BEE-HIVE BRAE

Ma daddy's at the pit
howkin coal wi his hauns
lik tatties.
Ma mammy says:
the creatur,
scrapin muck from his clothes.

In winter
when it's snowin,
we take turns doon the brae:
school-bags for sleighs.

Summertime, catchin bees
in jeelie jaurs.
The lids have holes.
But the bees always die.

Kenneth Steven

KITTENS

In the dark of the shed the tractor slept
Like a Cyclops. Outside, spring fields lay dazed in light,
The hills were tugged by gusts of sleet.

I closed the door and listened. Nothing.
Then I heard the tiniest sound, a searching,
Over there at the back of the darkness.

I crept closer, bent, found them –
A tangle of mewing and trembling –
Three rickety bags of milk and a mother,

Their eyes nothing more than cuts
In the dung-dark of the shed. I knelt and lifted them,
Black scraps of softness,

Their purrs throbbing their ribs,
Louder even than the snow wind
Snarling the door.

Born at the beginning of the year
In the banging cold of March
On the edge of the Highlands;

Unwanted things that would limp
From winter to winter by mice,
And the odd kindness of a farmer's wife.

Tia Thomson

THESE GENTLE DAYS

Sometimes
like tiny white ashes
the snow falls
so tentatively swirling
you could miss every flake
just blinking the way we do:

Without being warmed through,
the chill of disappointments
melted, the inferno cooled,
we could not feel
(accurately, instinctively)
this grateful sense that though
unused, we are deserving
of gentle days in their turn.

Valerie Thornton

IN CAHOOTS WITH ALLAH

I confess I have offended Allah:
my Persian cat's half moggy
and my Persian rug's from Belgium
and not hand-knotted wool or silk

but moth-proof synthetic.
It's a rarity in Persian rugs
being green, his sacred colour,
meant only for accents.

Despite a subtle flaw
which proves that Allah
didn't make the rug himself,
a plague of moths moves in,

pale as oats, puffing into powder
bloodless, on walls, skirting, floorboards,
fingers. I excavate their red carpet source
below everything in the cupboard:

a hoard of old eggs, burgundy grub-shit,
curling white worms, grubby cocoons,
bare threads and that peculiar smell.
And in the other cupboard,

and under the dark side of the bed.
All purged. Yet still they catch the light
on mellow evenings, scraps of tussore silk
flickering, unextinguishable, everywhere.

Today, Allah has relented, revealing
the secret cache, behind the settee,
in the floorboard gaps, beside his rug
below a thick pelt of half-Persian fur.

IF ONLY COLL WERE TWO FLOORS DOWN

If only Coll
were two floors down
I could drive (for two hours)
to the Oban
of my front door,
sail down two flights
on the Lord of the Isles
(for three hours)
and walk on the machair
of the back court (for ever)
to the best beach
in the world.

The song of the seal
on the rocks over there
is drowned out
by the sirens
rising and falling
from stone streets.
The slow thunder
of wheely binmen
ebbs and flows
and the smell
of rotting oranges
eclipses acres of clover.

The thrumming
of Archie's lobster boat
is lost in the drum
of a washing machine,
a neighbour
repairing his window
hammers out
the wingbeat of a raven
and, though the rhythm
is right, that phone
will never master
the corncrake's croak.

But you are here
on the southern beach
of this island of city
where later
in the cool of evening
we'll bathe
sleek as seals
in our waves
and whisper softer
than the raven's wing
to charm the short night
slow and long.

Gael Turnbull

THE LADY WHO LIKED TO STROKE FLOORS

She worked in the same office block, though wasn't with my firm. I noticed her polishing her car in the staff car park and made a flippant remark about seeing her face in it. She grinned.

'Oh, it's not the reflection that's important.'

A week or so later, on the weekend, I was coming back to my car after a visit to the Gallery of Modern Art when I was surprised to see her getting out of hers, apparently just arriving.

I regretted my silly remark on our previous encounter but she didn't seem to have held that against me and flashed a cheerful smile. Perhaps it was mostly the fine spring morning. As we passed each other she remarked, 'It's not the reflection, remember. It's the satisfaction of the contact.'

The full relevance of this, to anything or her presence there, was not obvious. That is, until later.

Our next encounter was a month or so after and entirely due to my thoughtlessness. I'd been doing a major 'shop' at the local supermarket and was coming out into the car park, pushing a trolley. What my mind was on I don't remember, but certainly not where I was going or the incoming traffic. She was just arriving and had to swerve and use her brakes which were luckily efficient.

As I recovered myself from the fright, she got out and came over. I apologised, 'Dreadfully sorry. Entirely my fault.'

'You were somewhere else!' she laughed. 'No...of course, you were here in front of my car. Very much NOT somewhere else. What strange expressions we use.'

I admitted, 'My attention was elsewhere.'

'Ah, yes,' she said, 'attention. Paying attention. Best to get it right. I like to get things right. Don't you? But it takes practice.'

I tried to shift the conversation into a more conventional pattern. 'We do seem to be running into each other rather often.'

'Or me running into you? Near enough anyway! Do you believe in coincidence?'

'It does happen, for whatever reason.'

'Another way of making contact. Or expressing it. Not necessarily random chance. But two things or events or persons that coincide. Simple enough!'

Her name was Frances but she called herself Fran, as did

everyone else, and was known for her combination of the apparently random and the very decisive. Though even she had her lapses.

A couple of weeks after that encounter I was slightly late getting away from work and one of the last out of the car park. A colleague ran out of her office holding a handbag.

'You know Fran, don't you?' she called. I admitted that we'd met and that I'd recognise her. 'She lives just around the corner from you and she's left her handbag with all her papers and credit cards. May not even have realised yet. Can you drop it off for her?' She gave me the exact address.

Other than a slight instinctive wariness, I could see no serious objection or problem, and found her address easily, and was even able to park almost directly in front of the main door to her stair. I pressed the buzzer for her flat and explained that I'd come to deliver her handbag.

She didn't seem surprised and just pressed her buzzer to release the door catch. When I got up to her door on the second floor, it was slightly open. I knocked and heard her voice, 'Come in!'

She was in the sitting room, crouched on the floor. The carpets were rolled back and the furniture pushed against the wall. There was a strong smell of wax polish and some aromatic oil.

I set down the handbag and as I stepped into the room nearly fell over. The floor was most efficiently polished.

'Watch out!' she called. 'I've worked hard to get that finish.' I reflected that it had nearly finished me but decided that such banter might be risky.

She seemed uninterested in the handbag and was busy admiring her floor. 'Even beats the finish on —— ' and she mentioned a well-known sculpture at the Art Gallery. 'I often go, when I'm near, just to give it a stroke. Of course, only when no one is looking and I'm ever so careful. Best way to really appreciate a sculpture. Or anything.'

I could see that she was watching my reaction which must have been satisfactory as she went on, 'And of course, it's the only way to really get to know a floor. I mean smoothing and oiling and polishing it. Not falling on it.'

She gave another stroke. 'Isn't it lovely? Just feel for yourself.'

I made a trial touch and indeed a very sensual and silky finish it had.

'You need to get right down,' she said, 'to do it properly. There's lots of room here beside me. I'll show you how. Don't be afraid.' I lowered myself carefully down, rather hypnotised by the sight of her hands moving back and forth across the silken surface.

'It's the best way, the only way to get to know a floor. Isn't that a wonderful sensation? Here, I'll show you how.' Her hands were unexpectedly strong, with a slightly roughened texture that was not at all unpleasant. She slid my hand back and forth across the boards.

'The more you practise, the better it gets. There's nothing to equal stroking. I could do it all day, all night... Nothing like it. Except of course, *being* stroked. Would you like to try?'

She guided my hand. 'Mmm. Yes, just like that. It is agreeable, isn't it? One doesn't have to stop.'

Billy Watt

FOXGLOVES

Look closely. Pinkly.
A trembling column
of pouts and puckers,
each mouth with a tell-tale tag
just beneath that upper lip,
like a conger eel's.

But don't look too close
at the violet depths
in our mottled throats:
just imagine embrace.
Think raspberries,
think cherries. Sugared cream.

So impossibly beautiful,
pout-pink and purple,
a chorus from your
most perplexing dreams.
Imagine the cherubs
of the Sistine Chapel –
then delete everything
but the mouths. That's us.

We inhabit shady places.
Root shallowly in moistness
of sod. Leave our spikes
to do the other work.

VINE WEEVIL

We're on the march
but you'll never know
till it's too late.

That slice of torchlight
and we're curled and creamy,
or dark, dark pellets
between your fingers.

You can only wait
and take your chances.

A scuttle, a clamber.
Elbows on our heads
and a mottled tan to die for.
No need for males,
we can choose the time and place
to tuck our eggs down,

then detonate
disorderly grubs
that will gnaw your roots,
mine out your tubers.

Coming out after breakfast
with a coffee in your hand,
you'll stub your hopes
on our leftovers.

Helen Welsh

PURPLE IRIS

Your secret is out. Your
blood-tipped spear
revealed briefly in the
plangent air, oh
so bold you are.

Whose blood so rich
and royal? Surely a
Duncan or, in these
small feus, a
Bruce.

You are not alone,
but you are the one with
blood on your heart. Tomorrow
the spear will be gone,
your hands spread

in innocence, your friends on guard.
But tonight, a night surely for intrigue,
I found you out.
Confess.
Confess.

Brian Whittingham

NACHO-MUNCHERS AND DOLLY-GRIPS

At the 14 screen *Mega-Multiplex*

They crunch the popcorn carpet
flashing torches
like a night at the blitz
They seat chattering late arrivals
for the summer's *must-see* block-buster.

A cellophane-crinkler's
mobile, releases William Tell.

A big-gulp-slurper
advises the cellophane-crinkler...
'yir no supposed tae hiv that oan!',

A nacho-muncher
advises the big-gulp-slurper...
'Away an gie's peace,
you're noisier than the fuckin phone.'

And the hero
who's saving America
and therefore, the world,
makes his first reel appearance.

At the *Art-house Cinema*

The volume of audience murmur
decreases in synchronisation
with the dimming houselights.

They settle down
getting seriously comfortable
draping legs over seats

in preparation to watch...

The idiosyncratic, ironic dramatisation;
the delicious fictional concoction,
that bristles with emotional insight,
and drags the horror genre
away from its origins
by making its threat existential.

And at the film's closing
when the credits roll,
a silent audience disapproval
permeates the atmosphere
if someone dares leave early.

So...who are you when you go to see a film?
Are you a seasoned
cellophane-crinkling
ice-cream carton-scraping
big-gulp-slurping
hot-dog-chomping
nacho-muncher?

Or are you the one
that watches till the very end, for the dolly-grip roll-call,
satisfied you have done your duty?

Jim C. Wilson

UTTER

A poem is hovering in the southern sky,
its meaning waxing, waning, like the moon.
Its words could touch upon your hair, your mouth;
I just don't know, don't know how it will end,
and shifting cloud might make the substance thin.
All might come clear if only I could sleep.

My syntax cracks, words warp, unless I sleep,
yet when day fades I'm drawn towards that sky,
and stars which punctuate, while light gets thin.
Then I discern the crack across the moon.
I must just trap beginning, middle, end;
feel syllables evolve deep in my mouth.

But an aftertaste like panic fills my mouth
and there's no lullaby to induce sleep.
A single singing line would serve to end
this sense of senselessness. Give me the sky,
and bring me, please, the mystique of the moon
for me to make your perfect poem. A thin

insistent voice says no. The air seems thin,
my breathing slight and slow. My open mouth
would swallow down that cold November moon
but miracles don't come, nor soothing sleep.
Your sonnet tells of geese across the sky;
cycles and seasons, the world without end;

right now *my* poem is only glimmers. End-
ing now might stop my patience wearing thin.
I'd turn my back against the darkening sky,
erase all images, then hush my mouth.
Would I then descend into silent sleep?
Could I then resist the pull of the moon?

I have my doubts. And perhaps no choice. Moon-
light pervades this room; I brood on an end,
recall the beginning. There's time for sleep
when the lines are complete, the bone-thin
fingers of dawn draw near. And from my mouth,
my tongue, the words will fill my hungry sky.

You are my moon. When all of life seems thin,
love near an end, let your mouth touch my mouth,
utter the poem, speak the stars, breathe the sky.

Dawn Wood

MIDWINTER'S DAY, FLORIDA

You and I have been sitting on the lanai,
drinking a bottle of white zinfandel,
expecting everything, expecting nothing.
The rain is patting down the pine leaves,
the Spanish moss is wistfully trailing,
a pattern is tapping from the spouting. A ripple
becomes a tail, becomes a skull-light squirrel.
I am sketching it; you have set a Hershey chocolate
almond for its eye-bright interruption –
at once, we realise that this is common,
it will warrant nothing. The zinfandel,
in the event, is sweet and pink. The sky
is shortly raised, collapses into evening,
something between us is settling.

James W. Wood

FOR MY REPLACEMENT

for Sarah and Rupert

Look carefully at the edge of the desk
Where I pushed in pins every time
She said I had to work weekends. Observe
The 3D triangles scrawled all over my blotter,
A surer sign of boredom than the poems
Currently stored in my computer under
c:\windows\pwhim. Hold your breath
And count the minutes every time
Someone else's lunch spills over
The two-hour mark. And when you go
Out the door at night, remember
To turn out the lights and photocopier
And printer and fax and desklamp. But leave
The computer, with its cursor winking cheerily –
At least you can screw them by wasting electricity.

BIOGRAPHIES

After labouring for a few years, **Gregor Addison** attended Newbattle Abbey College and went on to Aberdeen University and Jordanhill College, studying both English and Gaelic. For the last five years he has taught at Clydebank College. He has been published in *Gairm* (*nach mair*), *Chapman* and the *Edinburgh Review*.

Tom Bryan was born in Canada, 1950. Long resident in Scotland, he lives in Caithness. A widely published and broadcast poet, short story writer and novelist, his work has appeared in several previous editions of *New Writing Scotland*.

Ann Burnett does a lot of script writing for schools' radio programmes in Scotland and Northern Ireland, but since giving up teaching, she can now concentrate on developing other areas of writing as well. She is at present working on a novel and tutoring creative writing groups.

Jim Carruth lives in Renfrewshire and is an active member of the Johnstone Writers Group. His work has been widely published in various UK anthologies and magazines. He is currently working on his first collection.

Colin Clark is a writer and book artist. He is currently working towards an MPhil in Creative Writing at the University of Glasgow under the tutelage of Alasdair Gray.

Ken Cockburn was born in Kirkcaldy in 1960. In 1999 he set up pocketbooks with Alec Finlay, and was the editor of *The Order of Things: an anthology of Scottish sound, pattern and concrete poems* (pocketbooks, 2001). He lives in Edinburgh, and works for the Scottish Poetry Library.

Allan Crosbie edited *Such Strange Joy: ten years of Shore Poets* (iynx publishing 2001). He was short-listed for a Forward Prize for best individual poem in 2001, and was awarded a SAC Writers Bursary in 1999. He was a runner-up in the 1998 Arvon/Daily Telegraph Poetry Competition.

Jenni Daiches was born in Chicago, and has lived in Scotland since 1971. Published poetry includes *Mediterranean* (Scottish Cultural Press) and contributions to mainly Scottish magazines and collections. As Jenni Calder writes on literary and historical subjects.

Robert Davidson's lyric suite 'Centring On A Woman's Voice' was performed at Highland Festival '01 – 'Dunbeath Water' is being scored by composer William Gilmour for HF '03 – 'Columba' was published in *Poetry Scotland* and performed at the Cromarty Book Festival '01 – 'Through The Eye' is forthcoming from diehard poetry.

John Drosten was born in Glasgow in 1947 and brought up in Argyll. After a lengthy sojourn in London in the civil service he now lives in Edinburgh but is hankering again for the wild west. His poems have appeared in a number of magazines.

Jane Forrest is a self-employed Creative Writing facilitator and artist, who can show people how to make pictures in two hours. Her passion is to see people rediscover their dignity through writing and art. Her workshops are aimed at people who say 'I can't write/make a picture', then do it.

Griselda Gordon was born in 1961 in West Lothian to Anglo-Scottish parents. She was educated in Edinburgh and St Andrews and read Arabic at Oxford. She is currently studying for an MPhil in Creative Writing at Glasgow University. She lives in rural Ayrshire with her husband and three young children.

Charlie Gracie is originally from Baillieston, Glasgow, and now lives with his family in Thornhill, near Stirling. He works with homeless people in Clackmannanshire. Writing short stories and poetry, he has had work published recently in *Twa Dugs*, *Pushing Out the Boat*, *Poetry Scotland* and *New Writing Scotland 19*.

Yvonne Gray lives in Orkney. She teaches English part time and is a keen musician. Her poems have appeared in *Rationed Air* (a collaboration with artist Carol Dunbar), *NWS 18* and *19*, *Cenrastus* and *Poetry Scotland*. She received a Writer's Bursary from the SAC in February 2002.

After the universities of Strathclyde and Glasgow, **Iain Fraser Grigor** spent a number of years as a fisherman. He subsequently worked as a journalist in Scotland for the *Sunday Times*, the *Daily Express* and the BBC.

Vivien Jones lives in Powfoot on the north Solway coast and is a mature student with the University of Glasgow: Crichton Campus in Dumfries where she is studying for an MA in Creative & Cultural Studies. She has been actively involved as a teacher in alternative education in Scotland, and is an early music player of viols and wind instruments.

Lis Lee – poet and playwright, of Anglo-Irish-Spanish parentage. Lived most of adult life in Scotland. Currently writes in Kelso, Borders. Work staged by Cross Country Theatre Company and Traverse Monday Lizard. Poetry becoming widely published: *Cutting Teeth*, the *Eildon Tree*, and *Ver Poets Vision On 2002* competition anthology.

Gerry Loose – poet and editor. Books include *The Elementary Particles* (1993); *a measure* (1996); *Eitgal* (2001). SAC Writing Fellow, Castlemilk 1995-1997; Poet in Residence, Botanic Gardens, Glasgow, 1999-2002. Managing Editor, Survivors' Poetry Scotland.

Irene Lotta (a pen-name of **Ruth Dunster**): born Inverness 1961, having taught in Florence and Glasgow she became involved in Survivors Poetry Scotland in the 1990s, editing *Goodbye Woodilee* and performing regularly onstage. She is currently a researcher with the Mental Health Foundation and is editing *Spring Into Fall*, an anthology of Survivor Writing from Kirkintilloch.

James McGonigal (b. 1947) works in teacher education and has co-edited anthologies of Scots-Irish writing, Scottish religious verse, and new Scottish writing for children. His poems were published in *Driven Home* (Mariscat Press).

Kathy McKean studied English and Theatre at Glasgow University, where she is currently completing an MLitt. She was commissioned to write *Becoming* by Nicola McCartney's Look Out and it was performed by Lucy McLellan. Kathy is a member of the Traverse Young Writers' Group and the Royal Court Young Writers' Programme.

D.S. Mackenzie is from Easter Ross and lives in London. He is the author of one novel: *The Truth of Stone* (Mainstream).

Kirsten McKenzie was born in Edinburgh in 1975. She graduated from St Andrew's University in 1997 in English Literature and Scottish History and is now working as a press officer for the Scottish Executive. She is due to have her first baby this year. This is her first published work.

Born in Glasgow in 1964, **Rob Mackenzie** now lives in Turin, Italy, with his wife Anne and baby daughter Alyssa. He works with the Waldensian Church Of Italy (a 12th Century heresy). He will soon complete his debut novel. His poems have been published in many obscure magazines.

Cathy Mary MacMillan: born in Glasgow 1/4/59. Adopted at six weeks by a middle-aged Lewis crofter and wife. Married with seven children, aged 5-21. Is currently on second year of a BA Degree course in Gaelic Language and Culture at Lews Castle College in Stornoway. Very active campaigner for Gaelic Language rights. Writes drama, poems and short stories for children.

Hugh McMillan teaches in Dumfries. His poetry and prose have been widely published in book form and in magazines and anthologies in Scotland and abroad.

Andrew McNeil: brought up in the East Neuk after being born in Toledo, Ohio. A poet both in Scots and English also working on short stories and novels. A first collection by Kettillionia. Resident in Dunfermline.

Andy Manders is from Highland Perthshire. Poet, educator and dad, his work appears in publications (including *New Writing Scotland 17* and *18*) and landscapes across Scotland.

Irfan Merchant lives in Edinburgh. His work is published in various magazines, and appears in *Wish I was Here* (pocketbooks) and *The Redbeck Anthology of British South Asian Poetry*.

Marion Fiona Morrison – born in Glen, Isle of Barra. Brought up in Glasgow and educated at St Gerard's School and Glasgow University. Lives in South Uist and is currently a Principal Teacher of Guidance at Sgoil Lionacleit, Benbecula. Enjoys reading and writing in English, Gaidhlig and French. These are her first published poems.

David Neilson, author of *XII from Catullus* (Mariscat) and original illustrator of *The Patter*, recently had the privilege of designing a celebratory publication for Edwin Morgan's eightieth birthday. *Robert the Vole* is an occasional and rather long-term project.

Kathleen O'Rourke lives in Glasgow, but was brought up (a long time ago) in Baillieston. She has just started to write – this is her first story.

Walter Perrie was born at Quarter, Lanarkshire (1949); was educated at Hamilton Academy and at Edinburgh and Stirling universities. He has just completed his seventh collection of poetry and is at work on a collection of philosophical fragments. He lives in the Perthshire village of Dunning.

Andrew Philip was born in 1975. He studied linguistics in Edinburgh, where he now lives. He ran the Scottish Poetry Library's Holyrood link scheme, is a member of Edinburgh's Shore Poets and a winner in the Scottish Book Trust's postcard poems competition 2002. Poems in *ibid*, *Chapman* and *Sou'wester* (USA).

Lydia Robb writes poetry and prose in both English and Scots. Has been published in various anthologies. Recipient of a number of literary prizes and awarded a Scottish Arts Council Writer's Bursary in 1998. Collection of poetry *Last Tango with Magritte* published by *Chapman*, Edinburgh, launched in 2001.

Hugh Clark Small: born in Newarthill, Lanarkshire in 1961. His work has appeared over the past decade in a wide variety of publications including *Edinburgh Review*, *Chapman*, *Northwords* and the late-lamented *West Coast Magazine*. He now lives and works in Edinburgh.

Julie Smith: from Craigneuk, Wishaw now living in Glasgow. Published in *Nerve, Cutting Teeth, Northwords, Irish Studies Review*. Joint winner of the Keith Wright Memorial Award 2000; awarded a bursary by the Scottish Arts Council in 2001 under the New Writers Scheme.

Kenneth Steven is a widely published novelist, poet and children's author. In 2002 his three novels forming *A Highland Trilogy* were published by Scottish Cultural Press. His poetry collection *Iona* appeared from Saint Andrew Press in 2000 and has become a best-selling title. The author is based in Dunkeld.

Tia Thomson: brought up in Glasgow, with Highland roots, now living in rural Nairnshire. Three children. Degree in English and Drama, Glasgow University. Writing since she was seven, but this is her first publication since the school magazine.

Valerie Thornton writes poems and short stories. She has been short-listed for the SoS / Macallan Prize, and has also published an award-winning creative-writing textbook, *Working Words* (Hodder). Her first collection of poems, *Catacoustics* (Mariscat) was published in 2000. She is currently Royal Literary Fund Fellow at Glasgow University.

Gael Turnbull's most recent publications are *Might a Shape of Words and other transmutations* (Mariscat) and, with the Association André Lazare, an 'object-poem': *Le Loup du Pic St-Loup*.

Billy Watt was born in Greenock and now lives in West Lothian, where he works at Broxburn Academy. He writes fiction and poetry and was first published in *New Writing Scotland 7*.

Helen Welsh lives in Dunfermline and works as a Development Manager at the local college. She is married with a twelve-year-old son and writes long and short fiction, poetry, drama and non-fiction. She is currently working on a text book, a crime novel, and a number of magazine articles.

Brian Whittingham: poet, fiction-writer, editor etc. Born in and resides in Glasgow. Most recent poetry collection, *The Old Man from Brooklyn and the Charing Cross Carpet*, published by Mariscat Press. Presently, freelancing and creative-writing lecturer at the Nautical College in Glasgow.

Jim C. Wilson is a poetry and prose writer. He is currently the Royal Literary Fund Writing Fellow for the Office of Lifelong Learning at Edinburgh University. A past winner of the Scottish International Poetry Competition, his most recent collection is *Cellos in Hell* (Chapman). He lives in East Lothian.

Dawn Wood was born in Omagh, County Tyrone in 1963. She moved to Dundee in 1986 where she works as a university lecturer. She has been writing poetry seriously since 1997.

James W. Wood was born in Paisley and went to school in Canada, then in Perthshire. His work has appeared in *Scotland on Sunday*, *The Times Literary Supplement*, *Critical Quarterly*, *First Pressings (*Faber, 1998*)*, *Verse*, *Lines Review*, *Chapman*, and many others. He lives in London and works as a press officer.